Brutal Kangaroo: WikiLeaks Verdict Against Josh Schulte, and Other Whistleblowers

by Matthew Russell Lee, July 2022

The curtains were drawn in Courtroom 15A, clipped together so that the Manhattan skyline outside couldn't be seen and no one could see in.

For the Central Intelligence Agency witnesses against Josh Schulte, accused of sending the CIA's hacking tools to Wikileaks, Judge Jesse Furman had ordered that the courtroom would be sealed.

Kurt Wheelock had opposed it; Judge Furman's order provided for two pool reporters to be let in, as long as they didn't describe the witnesses.

Kurt had become the pool, that day. There were no other reporters there. And he'd try not to break the rules. Before coming to cover this Southern District of New York courthouse, he'd been thrown out of the United Nations for covering it too closely, and showing that UN Secretary General Antonio Guterres didn't want shown. He'd try not to make that mistake again. But he'd write about it, here.

During the first trial of Josh Schulte, when the courtroom was declared sealed for CIA witnesses, Kurt Wheelock had stood outside by the elevators on the 14th floor of the U.S. District Court for the Southern District of New York, live-tweeting as much as he could about those who walked in or out.

Now for the trial, additional precautions were being taken. The new judge referred obliquely to some other courtroom where they had been meeting about classified information. And during the CIA witnesses' testimony in the second trial, which Wheelock's colleague Michael Randall Long had applied unsuccessfully to unseal, even the jurors would be asked to step out in advance.

Just the previous month during the We Build the Wall trial of Tim Shea, Kurt had live-tweeted a jury note that Judge Analisa Torres read out in open court. The jurors, 11 of them, called out a twelfth and named him: Roberto, Juror Number Four. Kurt tweeted that, then heard Judge Torres say, I want that stricken from the transcript. But live-tweeting was a form of transcript, and now it was too late. Kurt didn't like taking down articles or tweets (although he had done so, only once, when the prosecutors in the Larry Ray trial asked for the list

2

of Claudia Drury's prostitution clients to come down).

Now as the second trial approached, Kurt resolved not to cover jury selection, so as to not be tempted. He wasn't much interested in the opening statements either. It was the CIA witnesses that attracted, the forbidden or sealed fruit. How would he approach it differently than the first time around?

II.

A first step was to look back at how the first trial had been. Even with the sealing orders, Judge Crotty had allowed pool reporters into the courtroom for the CIA witnesses. And why not here? Why no public hearing?

Then there was the juror who had been kicked off, just before the verdict, for reading news about the case. Kurt had run down to the courthouse lobby to hear her out, then back up to live-tweet some more. Would that be possible this time? When the testimony began in earnest?

What was most surprising about Josh Schulte's first trial was how few people cared about it. While now described as the biggest leak ever, many days there were swaths of empty seats in Judge Crotty's courtroom. Few knew of the SCIF on the 9th floor much less went up there; the SCIF shared the floor with a small district office of Rep. Nidia Velasquez. People now following the case laughed at Schulte's complaints, about the broken laptop, no stamps, no commissionary.

Kurt often thought of where he had been when Schulte was arrested in 2017, after he was interviewed in the Pershing Square restaurant across from Grand Central. He was still in the UN then, though already getting targeted and perhaps over-reacting in a manner that might now be called Schultian.

Initially allowed out on bond and home confinement, Schulte was finally put into the MCC during the summer of 2018 - on July 3 of which Kurt was roughed up and throw out of the UN. One thrown out, another thrown in.

After months trying to cover the UN from the now being sold out public library on 46th Street, Kurt arrived down at the SDNY court, spending months getting accredited, having his phone and laptop taken away at the entrance, getting them out to go write his articles in the basement of the public library on East Broadway. It was then that he first heard of the SCIF case and decided to look into it. Now he was hooked, for round two and beyond.

III.

"These fine gentlemen," Josh Schulte pointed at the US Marshals who sat in back of him in court, "You will be seeing a lot of them."

The CIA Vault 7 leaks re-trial began after these 16 jurors were picked. In responding to the jury summons they'd had no idea it could be about petabytes of information, air-gapped split hard drives and fall-out from the nerf gun wars. But here they were.

Kurt Wheelock the blogger was in the back bench of the courtroom gallery when the last 16 were picked. He heard their names but didn't publish them, at least not on his blog or Twitter feed. He gave in to the white noise and did not try to listen through it.

But when it came time for sealed witnesses, he told himself, he would be opposing it again.

Schulte argued to Judge Furman that if the prosecutors now wouldn't stipulate that what

Wikileaks had published was in fact government information, why was he on trial? Why indeed. Some was and some wasn't. 1.4 petabytes of data had been seized.

"The back door was the front door," Schulte said. Some jurors shook their heads. Drifting Deadline was one program, Brutal Kangaroo another. Kurt thought that would make a good title for this story, the serial, the parallel tale told from the inside.

He had rushed back to New York when he heard the opening statements would be on the second day. A FlixBus from Washington, from midnight to four pm, a bad smell in the back of the bus and the roads being fixed even at this hour. It was another America.

In Philadelphia they stopped in front of the Federal court. Kurt wondered if they had a Press Room like the one in the SDNY where he worked, with two PACER terminals and a mini-fridge. Josh Schulte on 39th Street had owned, he told the jury, huge hard drives and played games on them. He was charged with child porn but said others had uploaded it. A libertarian had provided a venue for all things maligned elsewhere. But what were his politics?

In his opening statement Schulte cited Ukraine's Zelenskyy, perhaps ironically. He name-checked George Orwell and said he'd played a role in tracking down Osama Bin Laden. How did he compare, say, to Virgil Griffith who pleaded guilty at the last minute to charges of helping North Korea with crypto? This leak was treated more seriously. FBI Agent Evanchec called the leak's impact "devastating."

While the help to North Korea was all what might have been, or what still might be. The prosecutors wouldn't let Schulte plead that way, and he probably wouldn't take it. His notebooks, marked Attorney Client Privilege, spoke of an information war. But this trial would in fact be it.

Unsealing I

Schulte had filed a civil case against the Attorney General, then Jeff Sessions - but during the criminal retrial, most of it was still sealed. So Inner City Press filed a request to unseal it:

"Dear Judge Furman: Inner City Press is covering defendant Schulte's above-captioned criminal trial before this Court. As part of its reporting it sought to access filings in the civil case Schulte v.

Attorney General, 19-cv-3346 (JMF) but found for many of them the response in PACER, 'You do not have permission to view this document.'

This is the case, for example, for Dkt No. 17, Schulte's April 22, 2022 letter to this Court, about 'inhumane confinement conditions and other issues stemming from the government's investigation [of] the WikiLeaks Vault 7 disclosures.'

It is also the case for Dkt No. 14, Affidavit Accompanying Motion for Permission to Appeal in Forma Pauperis; Dkt No. 8, regarding dismissal of motions in the case; Docket 6, Petition (Motion); Dkt No. 7, 'Plaintiff Petition to End Torture;' and even Dkt No. 5, a letter seeking a hearing on why these filings are sealed.

It is not clear at whose request these filings are sealed and not available to the public. This is a public / Press challenge to their withholding from the public. The right of access is not limited to criminal matters. See, e.g., *Lugosch v. Pyramid Co. of Onondaga*, 435 F.3d 110, 124 (2d Cir. 2006) (right of access applied to summary judgment motions in civil matter); and *In re Pineapple Antitrust Litig.*, No. 04 MD. 1628, 2015 WL 5439090, at *2 (SDNY 2015) ("There is.. no requirement that the application be made before the lawsuit is closed.")

Please confirm receipt & again docket this filing. Thank you.

Respectfully submitted, /s/ Matthew Russell Lee, Inner City Press

cc: charles.jacob at usdoj dot gov

On July 8, as the jury deliberated, Judge Furman docketed the request and ordered this:

"On July 5, 2022, Matthew Russell Lee, representing Inner City Press, submitted the attached request to unseal certain documents filed in this case. The case was sealed before being reassigned to the undersigned. The Court concludes that there is no reason for the majority of the docket to remain under seal, and it will now be unsealed. The sole exception is Plaintiff's submission at ECF No. 2-1, which is undergoing review. If, after review, the Court concludes that it need not be sealed, the Court will promptly enter an order unsealing it.

The Clerk of Court is directed to remove all viewing restrictions on the documents in this case, except ECF No. 2-1, which should remain under Court and participant view only. The Clerk of Court is further directed to mail a copy of this Order to Plaintiff in the Metropolitan Detention Center. SO ORDERED. (Signed by Judge Jesse M. Furman on 7/8/2022)."

Nearly immediately unsealed was Schulte's "Petition to End Torture" which asserted that "AG Jeffrey Sessions commits perjury." This, now unsealed, referred to an AG Sessions memo to the MCC of October 26, 2018. Digging, Kurt found it: 17 pages, starting with "Schulte is an individual with little respect for authority."

Then this: "The inmate shall not be permitted to speak, meet, correspond, or otherwise communicate with any member or representative of the news media in person, by telephone, by furnishing a recorded message, through the mail, his attorney, or a third party, or otherwise."

That triggered this book. Among those following the case, one wrote of the documents Inner City Press got unsealed, " That's nice. Also not news. How does that change that WL insiders acknowledge that Schulte blows their cover story?" What? And that those elsewhere for money uploading transcripts were funded by a foundation in Germany with a board member "named in WL operations." The AG Sessions measures on Schulte, a hundred yards from the SDNY Press Room where Kurt wrote this, had gotten lost and covered up in the wider politics. All Kurt could do for now, after unsealing, was this booklet.

Then there was the disparity between this official silencing of Schulte and the celebration of Snowden by some in the culture. The cast of the TV show Homeland had Snowden beamed in from Moscow. Mandy Pantinkin bemoaned the pain of exile for one so young, at 32 years old, saying, "But he's just a boy."

Clare Danes canceled a flight to hear the boy wonder speak. Schulte? Forgotten and reviled in windowless rooms in lower Manhattan and then Sunset Park. Maybe it was, as Kurt was told, because Schulte denied it. How could one be a whistleblower if one didn't just confess? To a lifetime of prison with this condition of silence? And so, a public trial, pro se. But would Schulte speak out? Could he?

Day 1

Assistant US Attorney David Denton: Joshua Schulte is responsible for the largest leak in CIA history, and put officers at risk. When confronted, he lied.

AUSA Denton: He stole custom-built software used to track terrorists. Those filed were posted on Wikileaks. It was devastating. Operations came to a crashing halt. Allies wondered if their info could be leaked. The FBI sprang into action

AUSA Denton: They found his man's crimes. He hacked and leaked cyber tools. Joshua Schulte was one of the CIA's own. He built the tools. He violated his oath to protect the US, and he violated the law. Why did he do it? Out of spite.

AUSA Denton: He felt the CIA had disrespected him. He wanted payback. His vendetta continued in jail. He got a cellphone in jail and leaked again, plotted a campaign. He committed espionage, computer hacking, and he lied to the FBI. My name is David Denton. AUSA Denton: Joshua Schulte built sophisticated cyber tools, in a secret building with armed guards. Those there were vetted, that they could be trusted.

AUSA Denton: Schulte was made a software administrator with super-access. He made back-ups... He falsely accused his co-worker of making a death threat. But the CIA found it was not true.

Schulte got angry and acted. The CIA locked it down, changed the codes

AUSA Denton: But the CIA did not change one particular key. And Schulte used it. He heard it too would be changed. That was the day he stole the info that Wikileaks posted. He used a snap shot, or reversion, before it was locked down.

AUSA Denton: He spent an hour inside the snapshot. He used his powers and copied the entire CIA cyber arsenal. He stole a complete copy - same as was published on Wikileaks. He unwound his reversion. Schulte started deleting log files. But he couldn't get them all

AUSA Denton: He downloaded software to hide his identity. He researched how to transfer, and how to destroy digital evidence at home. He tried to wipe his home computer clean - he followed the exact instructions of Wikileaks. He took a job in NY [at Bloomberg]

AUSA Denton: After Wikileaks published, Schulte lied to the FBI. Then, in jail, he used a secret phone to create accounts on social media. In jail notebooks he wrote, I will stage my information war

AUSA Denton: After Wikileaks published, Schulte lied to the FBI. Then, in jail, he used a secret phone to create accounts on social media. In jail notebooks he wrote, I will stage my information war

AUSA Denton: Ladies and gentlemen, you'll see how the agents identified Schulte and his back up version. Forensic experts will show you what he did. His digital fingerprints were all over it. They found the trail.

AUSA Denton: You'll hear from Schulte's co-workers, covert operatives at the CIA AUSA Denton: Schulte got the nickname "Nuclear Option." His mounting anger at the CIA, the agency tried to address it. You'll see the log files. You'll watch Defendant declare on video he wanted his supervisors to be punished. You'll see him in jail on the phone

AUSA Denton: He wrote that he would break of all diplomatic relations... At the end of the trial we'll talk to you again. For now, do three things. First, pay close attention. 2d, follow Judge Furman's instructions. 3d, Use your common sense - AUSA Denton: This man is guilty. Thank you.

Judge Furman: Now, defendant's opening statement.

Schulte: The evidence does not fit. There is no information war. I did not commit these crimes. Good afternoon. My name is Josh Schulte. I was born in 1988 in Texas.

Schulte: I worked at IBM. Then I wanted to serve my country. I was 12 yrs old on September 11, 2001. I applied to NSA and CIA after one semester. After successful background checks I was hired in 2010. I assisted on a case to verify the location of Osama Bin Laden

Schulte: I then worked at Bloomberg LLP. I was there when Wikileaks published. It was embarrassing for the CIA. They did not know when it was taken, how much or who. They still don't know. DEVLAN was so insecure it was nicknamed the Wild Wild West

Schulte: The evidence will show that an individual, after Snowden's leaks, said it could happen to DEVLAN. It was impossible to find the leaker. They could not admit it. To save face, they had to blame someone. They selected me as the patsy.

Schulte: The CIA told the FBI to go after me. This was a political witch hunt from day one. The government is manipulating the data. If you miss a day at work, they say you were committing a crime. It's spin and manipulation.

Schulte: This is the government's twilight zone. There were innocent explanations for everything. The first aspect of the government's fantasy is my motive. By 2016, sure life had given me lemons. But I made lemonade.

Schulte: They say I was driven to insanity. I stood up for myself. When I lost, I moved on with my life. Why Wikileaks? Why not just on the Internet to expose everything. Wikileaks only published a small segment of it.

Schulte: This does not jibe with my loyal personality and patriotism. The government says I broke the rules of the CIA. But there were no rules on DEVLAN. But it was just a co-worker, using his access to power. They try to conflate servers and permissions.

Schulte: In reality, the back door was the front door. I would not have had to go back in time. It was all unsecure. They say the March 3, 2016 version was taken for emotional reasons. The computer I used at CIA was preserved. I could have wiped it.

Schulte: Their evidence proves my innocence. They have the logs. Not one was deleted. The commands were not executed. But they plan to convict me regardless of my innocence. Someone stole their crown jewels. It's not a good look for the CIA.

Schulte: My CIA work station shows I only connected to one drive and connected it to a write-blocker. My computer did not have the space to store the back ups. That's reasonable doubt. My CIA work station proves my innocence. Then they seized all my home computers

Schulte: I had huge servers. These are my habits and hobbies. I stayed up late. I was playing an online game. The evidence will prove my innocence. They will wave a back up file in your face. They don't know which one was stolen.

Schulte: The government claims that Wikileaks sat on the info for a whole year. Really? An organization that wants to spread news? Does the NYT sit on a story for a year? You release it. The timeline does not make sense.

Schulte: Yes, I am incarcerated. These fine gentlemen here are Marshals. You will see a lot of them. I have been in jail five years - you cannot know the pain.

Judge Furman: Move on.

Schulte: Uh, ok. I was suffering from strain and anxiety.

Schulte: I wanted to publish the Presumption of Innocence. And it was, on Facebook... Then, the CIA reclassified things. Then they accuse me of thought-crime. Orwell's 1984 was prophetic. My notebooks were labeled Attorney Client Privilege.

Schulte: The government cherry picks the evidence to deceive you. The info war was about my unclassified redress of grievances. President Zelenskyy of Ukraine has likewise engaged in an information war to gain hearts and minds

Schulte: I ask the jury to realize how serious this trial is. Treat me as you'd like to be treated. The government will go first for everything. At the end in summation they will go first AND last. You will find I am innocent. After 5 years, justice will be done.

IV -- The Jurors

Six of the sixteen Schulte jurors were Hispanic, or had Hispanic surnames. Castro, Flores, Rivera, Ramirez, Arenas and Castillo. Two perhaps were Asian: an Ong and also a Mister Tempuro. Or was it tempura?

Days before jury selection, Judge Furman had noted that a long story in the New Yorker magazine might mean more need for an overflow courtroom. But had the article and venue had any impact on which prospects got on the jury? The rate of subscription to the New York varied by group, and by borough. Kurt had tried not to listen to the jurors' answers - in fact, having to go to DC, he'd had no choice. But shouldn't they be told when the courtroom was sealed, and why? Shouldn't they be allowed to see the redactions? Schulte asked for that, but was denied.

During the Michael Avenatti criminal case, and Sarah Palin's civil one against the New York Times, there'd come about a daily ritual of walk and talk, footage to upload. Schulte on the other hand was given from the MDC jail into the courthouse basement. Once inside he could be escorted to the SCIF and back by secret passage ways. He was a rat that they had captured and were now putting on trial. Schulte told the jurors, Put yourself in my shoes. But could they do that? Could or would they take that leap?

V.

Josh Schulte had four years to prepare for this trial, to get ready to not only face but question his accusers. And today would be the first day. On the stand was FBI Agent Evanchec, who Tuesday afternoon and Wednesday morning on direct described how Schulte was the only suspect. How his hands had been shaking when they interviewed him in the Pershing Square restaurant. And how he said, Texans aren't traitors.

And how after AUSA Lockard said, No further questions, he was on. Good afternoon, Schulte told Evanchec, and got it returned.

Schulte asked about the CIA office where he had worked, which was usually described as top secret and in an undisclosed location. Schulte asked, Doesn't the CIA interview all applicant there?

Evanchec said he didn't know. Doesn't the building have a visitors' center? Again, Evanchec didn't know, said he was only concerned with the vaults where Schulte worked.

Schulte got Evanchec to say he was within earshot of a conversation of Mike Pompeo, then the Director of the CIA. But it wasn't nailed out - or at least, not year.

One juror, it emerged, worked for the TSA. There was a concern they might hear someone talking about the case as they walked through the gate. A narrow gate, that. Neither side objected, though some did online.

The LAN in DEVLAN didn't really mean Local Access Network, it emerged, since two overseas CIA offices could sign in. Passwords were shared; Evanchec agreed it was called a dirty network. How then to prove anything? Did the leak come from Confluence? Which days version had it come from? It seemed the date had changed.

Things got ragged as the afternoon wore on. Evanchec started saying, I don't recall, and no amount of "does this refresh your recollection" would get past it. Evanchec declined to be reminded of a trip to Baltimore, which might or might not come up later in the trial. Judge Furman cut in at one point and said the only pending question pending, does it refresh your recollection, whatever it is, even just a bowl of fettuccine alfredo.

To Kurt Wheelock, live-tweeting these exchanges as he had other trials like Avenatti's before this same Judge Furman, it echoed Avenatti's self represented story about the government's case being like a cockroach in a bowl of pasta. Some said Schulte had only converted to Islam to get better food in prison. But how would they know?

1st Witness: FBI Agent Richard Evanchec

AUSA: Where do you work now? Evanchec: In Dallas. North Texas. Before that I was in counter terrorism. And in NYC, counter intelligence squad 6. We thwarted foreign government's spying.

AUSA: What was your role in investigating Josh Schulte? Evanchec: I was one of the lead agents. AUSA: Do you see Mr. Schulte? Evanchec: He is there, white mask. He just waved. Wearing a beard. With a shaved head. AUSA: Let's talk about March 7, 2017.

Evanchec: Wikileaks released Vault 7... The impact was catastrophic. Our enemies now knew our capabilities. Operations overseas were brought to a complete halt. Innovation was taken offline completely.

 AUSA: Look at the item on the ledge next to you. Have you seen that item? Evanchec: It's an HP laptop with copy of the Vault 7 leak. Schulte: The defense objects. Judge Furman: Overruled. AUSA Michael Lockard: What is here in Exhibit 2?

Evanchec: This is from the CIA documents leaked in Vault 7. It says, "CIA Hacking Tools Revealed." AUSA Lockard: What is this? Evanchec: This is the user guide to Brutal Kangaroo, the cyber tool.

Evanchec (reading) "To infect thumb drives... Brutal Kangaroo and Drifting Deadline." A CIA designed thumb drive that could infect others. This paragraph is classified as secret.

 Judge Furman: What is the marking at the top? Evanchec: SECRET is the classification level. Then Not For Foreign Dissemination- even an ally. Judge Furman: Jurors, some documents are declassified for this trial. There are other issues I'll describe as they come up

AUSA Lockard: What is this? Evanchec: The chain of command Mr. Schulte was under. AUSA Lockard: The stolen information was from the Center for Cyber Intelligence? Evanchec: Yes.

AUSA Lockard: Is the location of CCI undisclosed? Evanchec: Yes. It is fortified. Evanchec: There was a full body turnstile. You had to enter a unique identification PIN. AUSA Lockard: Where was the Development Branch? Evanchec: On the 8th and 9th floor. AUSA Lockard: How did you get in? Evanchec: A unique card reader and PIN for each Vault.

AUSA Lockard: Let's turn to your investigation. Evanchec: It was a full investigation of Joshua Schulte. With over 100 agents. 1.4 petabytes of information. Unprecedented in FBI history.

AUSA Lockard (reading from a stipulation) "If called as a witness, a member of FBI CART with knowledge of the matter logged these hard drives into evidence."

AUSA Lockard: (reading from stipulation) "GX 100 is a CD with records of Joshua Adam Schulte... Jeremy Weber... Michael, GX 115... Amol, 116... and the floor plan of the CCI... portions of the defendant's CIA personnel file. 401-405, NDAs, 409, letter of warning

Judge Furman: Ladies and gentlemen, sorry for stealing three minutes of your time. We'll pick up tomorrow. You heard CIA employees referred to by first names only, or even other names altogether. It's will my permission. If you get COVID, contact us.

Judge Furman: Members of the public, please hold a few minutes, to not run into the jurors. Can we get a preview of witnesses? AUSA: Evanchec and cross will take up much of tomorrow. [And when the "sealed" witnesses? Watch this feed]

Judge Furman: Mr. Schulte, you'll be taken to the SCIF (Sensitized Classified Information Facility), please give the government your list. Also, you crossed the line in opening, essentially testifying. I want to warn you against it in your questioning

Judge Furman: You need to ask questions like a lawyer, not a witness. Schulte: I expect that documents will support me. Judge Furman: It was 1st hand testimonial. I'll leave it there. I'm told one of the jurors wants to speak to me. I'll bring it up tomorrow.

VI.

The day of opening arguments, interested was relatively high in the Schulte trial. Day 2, already, it was falling off. Someone said, of his beard, He looks like a terrorist. He converted, Kurt Wheelock countered. People needed something to do in jail besides practice their trial lawyer skills.

Kurt was fascinated by the nitty gritty of Schulte's day of interrogation and being searched. He'd left Bloomberg and gotten approached. No Miranda warning, no warning about the penalties for lying to an FBI agent. They took him to Pershing Square. Kurt had been there once and found it overpriced. They took him to his apartment on 39th Street - and where? - then told him to check into a hotel while they searched it.

What had Schulte told Bloomberg about his absence? If the CIA had been negligent in hiring him, what about Bloomberg. Good coding was good coding, it seemed. It was like the NFL, of which some wag said all winning teams need to felon. Or maybe that was a racist, who said it.

In the 15th floor hallways outside the courthouse, having stepped out to check on another case, Kurt ran into counsel saying What a jerk. Who did they mean? At the UN, they had used to say that about Kurt.

That was it, perhaps. Perhaps in some cases Kurt found something to identify with in the defendant.

It wasn't always possible, like the sex cultist Larry Ray. But here, it was possible. And so the re-trial was interesting, even more so that the first trial. But how to express it?

First cross-examination, of FBI Agent Evanchec:

Judge Furman: Cross examination.

Schulte (unmasking) Good afternoon.

Evanchec: Hello, Mr. Schulte.

Schulte: From the outset of your investigation, I was the only suspect?

Evanchec: You were the only one we could substantiate anything against.

Schulte: You had unfettered access to DEVLAN, correct?

Evanchec: Yes.

Schulte: You testified that the CCI office is in an undisclosed location, correct? Evanchec: Yes. Schulte: But DD1 is where the CIA brings all of its job applicants, right? Evanchec: It was not a topic of my investigation.

Schulte: You're saying the leak was from Confluence? Evanchec: Well, all but many a page of two. Schulte: But this is an important part of your investigation... I'm struggling to understand - you just don't remember, or you never figured out?

Evanchec: My involvement dwindled after our interactions. Schulte: So you just don't know. Evanchec: I'll leave my testimony at what I've said. Schulte: Pull up GX 5-2. At the bottom here it lists previous versions, correct? Evanchec: It does.

Schulte: So if Wikileaks received the March 6, 2016 version they could have selected the March 3 version, correct? AUSA Lockard: Objection (off mic) Judge Furman: Sustained. Please use the microphone. Schulte: Were you aware that malware could change file times?

Evanchec: I am not personally aware. Schulte: Did you ever speak with the director of the CIA about this case? Evanchec: I was in earshot of a conversation.

Schulte: Who was the director? Evanchec: Michael Pompeo. Schulte: Did you meet with the CIA on June 26, 2017?

Evanchec: I can't recall the dates. Schulte: Do you recall the CIA telling you to go after me with everything? Evanchec: I don't recall.

Schulte: What are link messages? Evanchec: Internal messages. Schulte: Do you recognize this?

Evanchec: Appears to be a transcript of instant messaging chats. Judge Furman: Say the exhibit number. Make a record. Schulte: DX 101-1. I'd like to publish this to the jury. AUSA: Objection. Judge: Sustained. Schulte: OK.

Schulte: Does it refresh your recollection about meeting with the CIA? Evanchec: No. Schulte: Does it refresh your recollection about going to Baltimore? AUSA: Objection. Judge Furman: Sustained. Schulte: OK. We met March 15, 2017, correct? Evanchec? Yes.

Schulte: And you and Agent Donaldson took me to the Pershing Square diner, right? Evanchec: Yes. Schulte: Did you give me a Miranda warning? Evanchec: No, we did not. Judge Furman: Jurors, this comes from Miranda v. Arizona [etc]

Schulte: Did you say this OIG email was classified? Evanchec: I did. Schulte: There's a big difference --

Judge Furman: Just ask a question. Schulte: Do you not think that I simply misunderstood what you were talking about? AUSA: Objection Judge Furman: Sustained

Schulte: You did not record our interview, right?
Evanchec: I did not. Schulte: Are you aware that
nearly all police departments not require body cam
video? AUSA: Objection. Judge Furman:
Sustained.

Schulte: So before you came to talk to me at
Bloomberg you selected Pershing Square diner,
correct?

Evanchec: I did not personally choose it. Schulte:
You had agents at Pershing Square diner and they
could have set up video or audio, right? Evanchec:
We could have

[After jury leaves]

Judge Furman: Mr. Schulte, while you're doing
better than I might have expected for someone with
no trial experience, please ask standby counsel
especially about refreshing recollection and getting
exhibits in. I see them handing you post-it notes.

[Cross continues next morning

Jury entering! Judge Furman: Juror 15, I take it that
my deputy conveyed to you... [A nod] Judge
Furman: Very good. Proceed, Mr. Schulte. Schulte:
Good morning. Yesterday you testified about the

search of my Manhattan apartment. How many agents? Evanchec: 8 to 15.

Schulte: How long did you take? FBI Agent Evanchec: 14 to 15 hours. Schulte: For a one bedroom apartment? Evanchec: Yes.

Schulte: You seized all the electronics - how many? Evanchec: Two servers, desk tops, thumb drives, hard drives...

Schulte: There was no National Defense Information discovered on my mp3 players, correct?

Evanchec: Not that I recall.

Judge Furman: Jurors, National Defense Information is a legal term. You'll decide it is or isn't.

Schulte: Was there any classification review by the CIA of the IRC chats?

Evanchec: I don't recall.

Schulte: You seized 20 terabytes of data to try to find anything on me, correct? Evanchec: That is not the goal of our investigations.

Schulte: Your search warrants for GitHub and Reddit, you found no National Defense Information, correct?

Evanchec: No we did not. Schulte: And here you found a movie, Robin Hood with Kevin Costner, correct? Evanchec: Correct.

Schulte: You said you found documents in the headboard of my bed, right? All my CIA documents?

Evanchec: Most of them. Schulte: Like my CIA pay stubs. A: Yes. Schulte: And just because an email has full names doesn't mean it's classified, right? A: It might be.

Schulte: Your notes here, they contain the last names of covert operatives of the CIA, correct? Evanchec: Well, just one. Schulte: But that's a violation, isn't it? Evanchec: I'm not a classification authority. Schulte: Did you purposefully disclose NDI?

AUSA Lockard: Objection!

Judge Furman: Sustained.

Schulte: But the government never charged you with a crime, correct? AUSA: Objection. Judge:

Sustained. Schulte: Let's talk about Google searches.

Schulte: During this time period, Wikileaks released the DNC emails, right? Evanchec: Yes. Schulte: And there was a fiasco with your director, Comey, right? There was Guccifer 2.0, right?

Judge Furman: Do you know what Guccifer 2.0 is? Evanchec: No, sir.

Schulte: There were also the Shadow Brokers... Is it your understanding that Wikileaks has NSA code?

Evanchec: I do not know about that. Schulte: Did you know that 80% of the searches you claim I made about Wikileaks were not in fact searches at all? Evanchec: No.

Schulte: Are you aware of Google News? Evanchec: I do not not regularly use Google - so, no. Schulte: Did you know Google makes a special log in your search history when you're using Google News? Evanchec: No.

VII.

Kurt Wheelock had fought against the sealed courtroom protocols but now they had arrived.

Thursday morning before the jury came in, Judge Furman said that for the coming witness, most people would have to leave the courtroom. Along with Schulte's mother and father, there in the second row, there were two other exception, initially won before the first trial's judge, Paul Crotty. And Kurt would be one of them.

Schulte said he had 45 minutes of cross examination left. But it went longer, with Schulte asking FBI agent Evanchec if his Google Searches - which he pointed out include Google News alert auto notifications - might not have been tied to other Wikileaks news, from the DNC emails to Guccifer 2.0.

Judge Furman cut in and asked Evanchec, Do you know about Guccifer 2.0?

No, Evanchec said. He also didn't know how Google News alerts worked. Schulte make the point was it was stricken from the record.

Finally at 12:20 pm it began. Kurt was told, Get out of the hallway (so that the CIA witness could enter unseen). But then he was allowed in. "What paper are you with?" he was asked.

"Inner City Press," he said. "And it's not on paper."

The CIA witness, who it's fair to say was short, came in front the front door. Not the holding cell, nor the judges' elevator. Maybe he'd been driven in through the basement garage. Kurt couldn't be in two places at once.

He said his name, in open court: Anthony Leonis. He had been Schulte's supervisor. And he'd quickly concluded that Schulte couldn't be trust. They moved his cubicle, then his unit, then took away his access to OSB Libraries.

This one, Schulte had reversed through Atlassian. That sent off alarm bells, and the whole library was taken away to a third party administrator But it was announced not by the new outside administrator but rather one of Schulte's colleagues. In the emails were Jeremy, Sean, Richard, Debra, Bonnie B. Smith, Frank Stedman, Leonard Small and Patrick Schaffer.

VIII.

In the gallery of the emptied-out courtroom Kurt Wheelock moved to the side with the exhibits screen, right behind Judge Furman's law clerks. From there he took notes on the emails shown on the screen, many with names re-written in white on previously redacted spaces: Debra, Bonnie B. Smith, Frank Stedman, Leonard Small, Patrick Schaffer

One last name, perhaps among there or perhaps not, should have been redacted, it was said. Only the exhibits that were sent in to the jury, weeks from now, would become public. The prosecutors, unlike in the Larry Ray sex cult case, weren't making available the exhibits, at least not yet. Maybe there was not the demand.

The jurors looked interested, especially a juror in Nike pants in the second row, leaning forward and watching Schulte as he questioned, Evanchec as he answered. Yes, they had surveilled Schulte on vacation in San Diego, Starbucks with his mother. How would this play with the jurors? Kurt would follow up to know.

IX.

Josh Schulte had landed a few blows on FBI agent Evanchec. But how would he do against his former supervisor at the CIA, Anthony Leonis?

It started well enough, with Schulte showing the Leonis had never managed people before he worked at the CIA. (Judge Furman did not allow him to ask where it was that Leonis had worked). But the things go too personal, or surreal. Schulte asked, You never spoke with me before you wrote me up, right?

We planned to speak with you, Leonis said calmly. He had prepared for this.

But your memo was already written, Schulte demanded.

There was no memo, Leonis said.

Schulte looked at the jury and back. "No memo?"

Leonis smirked. "It was a memorandum," he said.

Kurt Wheelock thought, this can't be helping the prosecution with the jury. But soon Schulte was getting half of his questioned objected to, and Judge Furman was sustaining the objections.

The US objected to Schulte saying "Foreign Office West," and revealing a location. There had been two overseas offices connected to the supposed Local access network, DEVLAN.

"Move it along, Mr. Schulte," the judge said. The CIA wanted to get Leonis out of town by nightfall.

And they did, and even put a Microsoft expert, then at MITRE, on the stand. It would be long weekend for Schulte in the MDC. And Wheelock vowed he would try to learn more about the roots of all this leaking, before considering his own.

X.

In the sealed courtroom CIA supervisor Anthony Leonis described the step by step identification and exclusion of Josh Schulte in the cyber tools division.

They ordered him to move cubicles, then to a different floor of the Northern Virginia buildings they insisted was in a secret location though it had a visitor's center.

They cut his access as an administrator to Brutal Kangaroo, then cut his access all together. But they forgot and left him a key. If in fact he had sent Vault 7 to Wikileaks, would it have been any surprise?

Kurt found himself identifying with Schulte, charged not only with leaking National Defense Information but also child porn, not because of either but because of this mundane Stations of the

Cross in a cliquish workplace, or place of work as the UN had been to Kurt from 2006 to 2018.

In 2011 the UN Correspondents Association tried to thrown Kurt out, due to his reporting on this blog that the President of UNCA Giampaolo Pioli had rented one of his apartments to a Sri Lankan war criminal then gave an UNCA screening to a Lankan war crimes denial film.

For weeks Kurt had been forced to sit in a windowless room over the UN Library and listen to the charges, to the demand he take the story down and apologize. He refused. But they just barely missed having enough votes to through his out. He wrote about that to – then quit and started something called FUNCA, the Free UN Coalition for Access.

But it wasn't over. They kept gunning for him and once Antonio Guterres because Secretary General, with the support of and secret side deal with China, they had an ally as contemptuous of free press as they were.

When UNCA held its private annual meeting in the UN Briefing Room, Kurt announced that he would stay in the room and film it, since it was the briefing room. The UN-ites yelled at him through the glass of the interpreters booth as he live streamed, and called in Spokesperson Stephane Dujarric and his wormy deputy Farhan Haq to order him out.

Kurt said, I'll only leave if Security tells me to. If I start letting the spokesman tell me to leave the briefing room, you'll do it every day. (Ultimately, they would).

When the UN Security guard came and robotically told Kurt to leave, citing Dujarric, he left. But soon he got a letter telling him to clean out his shared office in the UN. He said he was still working, and a guard named McNulty frog marched him out.

For three days he reported on the UN from a bench in the park across the street. Business Insider visited him and wrote about it. The UN, through Dujarric, virtually begged him to come back in as they were being accused of censorship. Later, Team Guterres wouldn't care. They were legally immune, flush with Chinese cash and full of hot air about climate change.

Once back in, Kurt's movement were restricted. He couldn't access the second floor where not only the Security Council but also ECOSOC and

General Assembly were. He had to get a MALU minder, who would stand next to him and ask, Who are you trying to interview? A leaker, of course.

UN Security took to building a blue ribboned stantion pen around him, so no one would speak to him. He filmed it all.

Finally one night when the UN Budget Committee was meeting, Kurt passed by at 10 pm to do a final interview before leaving for the night. He questioned Tommo Monthe the Ambassador of Cameroon, then murdering Anglophones in the North- and South-west regions. Then UN Security, which had it emerged been surveilling him,grabbed him and threw him out. They tore his shirt, twisted his arm and broke his laptop.

The next day he was refused entry altogether. The NYPD precinct on 51st Street said there was nothing they could do, the UN has immunity. They took down a handwritten complaint but it never went anywhere; the FOIL requests are still pending.

Kurt covered the UN from the sidewalk that summer, then the 46th library (now closing) in winter. From above a Korean deli on 45th Street he wrote to Senators, but none of them did anything except put him on the email list for their propaganda and and fundraising requests.

Finally Kurt began covering the SDNY courthouse and got accredited there, with a cubicle and a PACER terminal and a fire stairway where daily he filmed and ranted at the UN noon briefing, then tweeted it out. He emailed questions to the UN each morning, but now they never answered any of them. He got the Quinn Emanuel law firm, pro bono, to write to Guterres' head of accreditation about a process to get him back in. No answer at all. The UN was immune and did nothing.

Yes, Kurt could identify with Josh Schulte. He just hadn't had any National Defense Information to leak.

But he did have a story, or stories...

Interlude I

In the retrial of Joshua Schulte for exfiltrating Vault 7 from the CIA to Wikileaks, the courtroom was sealed for the CIA witnesses so that no one could see or report what they looked like. The exception was for two pool reporters. Kurt Wheelock was one of them - the only one, in fact. No one else, it seemed, cared.

Beyond the sealing of the courtroom, the names of the CIA witnesses and even those cited in testimony or exhibits were shortened or outright changed. One exception was the first CIA witness, Anthony Leonis.

Kurt was in the gallery of Courtroom 15A, right behind Schulte's parents, while Leonis was on the witness stand. He won't be physically described here but his manner was bureaucratic. He repeatedly said, This wasn't the type of human resources problem you wanted in your third week on the job.

Leonis seemed to mean, his third week as a supervisor of a branch in the CIA's CCI. But when Schulte, representing himself though with a slew of Post-in(TM) notes and whispered instructions from his stand-by counsel, asked Leonis where he worked before being at the CIA, Assistant US Attorney Michael Lockard shouted, "Objection!"

Judge Jesse M. Furman quickly said, "Sustained. Mr. Schulte, remember what we said at sidebar." The sidebar had taken place with white noise, even in the sealed courtroom. And that was it. Schulte moved on.

But Kurt Wheelock didn't.

As soon as he got back in the Press Room, Kurt in Incognito Mode whatever its utility Googled Anthony Leonis, since they'd said that was his real name. There was one who'd graduated from high school in California and played baseball there. An older man, with the same name, had died there at 80 years old. Father of the CIA agent?

There was an Anthony Leonis who had been a Human Resources specialist for 35 years. Too old, despite the H.R. irony.

Then Kurt remembered where he'd heard the name.

It was on his last job, or beat. At the United Nations, from which he was now banned from even entering as a tourist. One of the cronies of Secretary General Antonio Guterres had mentioned, during one of Guterres' many vacuous photo ops, a project they were working on with: Anthony Leonis.

Kurt had written the name down on the back of a Metro North Railroad ticket stub in his back pocket as soon as he came downstairs from the 38th floor, sitting in the glassed-in focus booth he'd taken to working in after they evicted him from his UN office. He'd transferred the name to the reporter's notebook he kept, same as he did now.

But why would the United Nations, or at least its boss Tony Guterres, be working with a US CIA officer? A spook, a spy, a hacker? Was this Tony helper the same Tony Leonis as in the sealed courtroom, with its heavy drapes held closed with the big black clips Kurt's friend Michael Randall Long still used on legal pleading when they got too long? Even as the re-trial of Josh Schulte rumbled on, or even if it progress into a third trial on the nasty images charges, Kurt would follow it up. But he would need help from Michael Randall Long. They would be at it again.

The first step would be to try to get the UNTV video of the photo op where Kurt Wheelock had overheard the reference to Anthony Leonis. Kurt had jotted it on the train ticket then into his daily pad. When they'd thrown him out of the UN the last time,they hadn't let him take anything with him, or come back in to get it. Instead a bureaucrat name Tal Mekel had repeatedly texted him, on behalf of UN censor-in-chief Melissa Fleming, asking where it should all be mailed.

Kurt had the crazy idea that if he didn't accept his stuff, it wouldn't be final,they'd have to let him back in. So at first he'd dodged the texts, or answered them obliquely. But finally Mekel said they would be throwing it all out in a week's time. And while a US government agency or even private employer would probably not do this, due to fear of being sued and paying damages, no one could sue the UN. So Kurt responded.

Five big boxes were mailed to Kurt. Inside them were his note pads, perhaps photographed and catalogued by the UN but now still intact. And it took hours, looking day by day, to find the notation "Anthony Leonis" from the photo op. But now Kurt had the date.

Even banned from the UN, UNTV still emailed him daily links to download video of the noon briefing at which the questions Kurt emailed in never got answered. Maybe they hadn't gotten the memo; maybe this was the UN's own concession, or way to say internally they were not barring him from covering the UN. But would this UNTV unit, housed in the third sub-basement of the Glass House with windows facing the FDR Drive and the river, still have this old video?

Kurt emailed then and at first there was not response. Then this, from a Burmese guy who made a good living off the taxpayers doing very little, so 99% of UNTV video, no one cared to see more than once, if that. "You're lucky," the Burmese guy wrote. "That one, we still have."

* * *

Kurt Wheelock was alone at the PACER terminal. Everyone else had left, while he was out at the gym in the housing projects by the river. He liked the silence, other than the once an evening visit by the Court Security Officer on duty, making his round. Kurt knew them now, and waved and greeted them without turning around.

He downloaded the video that the Burmese guy had sent. It was longer than for most photo ops - and the sound was on from the beginning. When Kurt turned the volume all the way up, and played it again and again, he heard that four others beyond Anthony Leonis were mentioned. A group of five at the UN - where else was that the pattern?

* * *

When Kurt Wheelock explained the pattern of the five to Michael Randall Long, in his law office over the Ali Baba fruit stand on Worth Street, Long was excited. When Kurt explained the work that only he and not Kurt could do, less so. "Or my designee," Long said.

47

"It's better if it's you," Kurt said. "Lawyer and all."

Long slightly knew a woman in the U.S. State Department named Laurel Rapp. Another lawyer had introduced - one who had done a bit a work of Kurt's case, if it was a case, as it happened. But since the lead allegation here was that the US CIA was working with the CIA, it seemed clear to Long that the best initial approach would be to others of the five, two in particular.

Kurt was more cautious. "If you approach the Russian Mission right now, with what's going on in Ukraine, who knows how it and we could be used."

Long nodded. "So how about China?"

Kurt said, "Just don't mention anything about me. I'm as much banned from the Chinese Mission and China as I am from the UN. They've very close."

"Tell you what," Long said. "I'll try France first. If that fails, I'll try China. With the UK being out of the European Union, and BoJo on the ropes due to party-gate and now censoring the press, I'll leave them for absolute last."

Long looked through the UN's Blue Book of diplomatic representative and entering the contacts of the general counsel of the French Mission to the

UN into his phone. He'd make the outreach later, after an appearance in the SDNY Magistrates Court.

* * *

Michael Randall Long got his client released on bond in the Magistrates Court, then took the subway up to Grand Central to meet the French Ambassador. When he'd called the Mission's general counsel and explained what his inquiry was about - unconfirmed reports that France had spies embedded in the UN Secretariat of Antonio Guterres - the call had been transfered to the Ambassador himself, Nicolas de Riviere.

Kurt Wheelock told Long that he was called Flippy Nick, both because of his fopping hairdo and his arrogant dismissal of any criticism of France or, mostly, himself. But Long went into it open minded, signing in at the One Dag skyscraper and taking the elevator up.

He was show into Flippy Nick's corner office, looking out over the UN and Queens and Long Island behind it. "Let me make one thing clear," Flippy Nick said. "The French Republic is the strongest supporter the United Nations has. Also the Secretary General. He is a good European."

"I don't doubt it," Long replied. "But from what I'm hearing, France uses UN humanitarian offices, mostly in Africa, to spy on its opponents."

"It is not we who have opponent," de Riviere corrected. "There are long standing presidents in Africa who, if they fall, will be replaced by terrorists, jihadists. We are doing the UN's work for it, really. The Security Council's."

"Then why not do it through the Security Council?" Long asked. "Why not put it before the 15 members and get a vote of approval?"

Flippy Nick smirked. "It is not so easy for the A-3, the African members. They cannot be seen as giving in to neo-colonialism, or what they call FrancAfrique. And do we it it ourselves. The Five."

"And the other four, what do they get out of it?" Long asked.

"Each one has her concern," Nicolas de Rivere said. "Right now our British friends are concerned about criticism of their plan to sent refugees to Rwanda. China, of course, wants minerals and to make its exhorbitant loans. Russia?" He laughed. "They want to send the mercenaries of the Wagner Group but now they find they need them in Ukraine."

Long nodded. "And my country, America?"

"Yes, your country. Right now the new administrations, it seems they are not comfortable with this way of doing business." He paused. "If you do not mind, they are buffoons. This school boy, Antony without the H, he is like a virgin. But there are others in Washington who understand."

"Like who?

"Bill Burns," Flippy Nick replied. "I worked with him on the Iran deal, the P5 plus One. Burns, he understands."

Long asked, "And Antonio Guterres?"

Flipp Nick stood up from behind his desk, and looked out over the UN. "He is the beneficiary of the brotherhood of the Five. We chose him because he says nothing about it, or about anything we do. It is embarrassing sometimes, like on what China is doing to the Uighurs, or Russian to Urkaine, at least at the beginning. All five of us ultimately told him to speak up a little. Not much, but about food, sure, and energy. Otherwise our game would be exposed." He paused. "And now, of this we shall speak no more, mon ami. If any of this is repeated I will deny it. And you will deal with the less friendly of the Five."

"Mais bien sur," Michael Randall Long said. And with that the meeting was over.

End of Interlude I

First sealed witness:

OK - "sealed" session about to begin ... [Later] Whew - out of sealed courtroom after 2 1/2 hours. "Now it can be told" - well, sort of -- The witness, who cannot be physically described under the order, is Anthony Leonis. He was Schulte's supervisor. He identified Schulte as "the man with the shaved head"

Leonis: On March 7, 2017 I was supposed to drive my boss, I was looking forward to the time to talk - but the Vault 7 leak came out on Wikileaks and they said, everyone to the office! There, the conference room was full. Brutal Kangaroo could no longer be usedAUSA Denton showed on the screen the Brutal Kangaroo / Drifting Deadline users' guide.

AUSA Denton: What is air gap jumping? Leonis: A thumb drive infects one computer, and it spreads onto another thumb drive. On the screen: EZCheese LinkFiles / Giraffe Links

Questioning turns back to the decision to relocate Schulte after restraining order against Amol. Email to Schulte: "As discussed, please move to your cubicle." Josh = 9W53-020 Emails involved Debra, Bonnie B. Smith, Frank Stedman, Leonard Small, Patrick Schaffer

Then moving cubicles deemed not enough. Josh to AED/RDB (under Leonis), Amol AED/MDB. Schulte responds with emails that he assumes this is punishment for reporting Amol and getting the protective order. He gets no written answer; writes again.

Schulte was allowed to contribute to, but not administer, OSB Libraries. But, Leonis complains, he still did - & told Jeremy he'd been authorized. Alert! Leonis says he began to consider stripping all of Schulte's access. [A bureaucratic stations of the Cross]

Schulte did not get to start cross examination of Leonis today. AUSA Denton said he has an hour more of direct. So, 10 am tomorrow, the cross.

[Next morning]

On June 17, Leonis finished his direct and was cross examined by Schulte, with a deadline to finish before the end of the trial day. Inner City Press live tweeted it here:

CIA' Leonis: Josh told me he was going to fight back. It caught me off guard. He was going to put up a fight about a management decision. That's not the way people talk in a professional environment.

AUSA: Did you ever retaliate against him? Leonis: No. AUSA: Mr. Schulte wrote he has incurred the wrath of his supervisor Karen. How was Karen?

CIA's Leonis: Karen cared so much about people. She'd walk the halls and ask you about your family... We asked Josh and Amol to go to the Employee Assistance Program

Leonis: This not the kind of thing you want to deal with, 3 weeks into a job [as supervisor]. I just wanted to help people build tools to collect intelligence for our country. AUSA: Is there classified info in this email? Leonis: The 3d graf talks about developers

Leonis: And it talks about a vulnerability in one of our network. And it talks about foreign office West. So it gave the location. And it had the name of an undercover officer. So in my read, it is not unclassified.

Judge Furman: Jurors, I approved the substitution of the phrase "Foreign Office West" for the actual location. Just so you understand. Leonis: After Vault 7 was published, we became a crime scene. The investigators bought cameras into the SCIF, which was strange AUSA: No further questions.

Judge Furman: Cross-examination.

Schulte: Good morning. CIA's Leonis: Good morning.

Schulte: Didn't I have a great relationship with my management before you? Leonis: I can't say. Schulte: You didn't have my file? Leonis: No.

Schulte: I was promoted every year until my last year, right? Leonis: I don't know.

Schulte: You didn't have access to promotion records? Leonis: I don't remember. Schulte: But you began keeping a dossier (says the "R") on me, in a white binder, right? Leonis: No.

 Schulte: You never kept a white binder? Leonis: Later we did. Schulte: Before you became a manager at the CIA, where did you work before? AUSA: Objection! Judge Furman: Sustained. Schulte: Had you ever managed people? Leonis: No.

Schulte: Did you ever get training on conflict resolution? CIA Leonis: I had experience in getting people to sit down and talk. Schulte: Just hash things out.. When Jeremy Weber wrote to you, not copying me, did you know he had stopped talking with me? Leonis: No. Schulte: So this email that Mr. Weber sent --

Leonis: Mr. Weber should not have sent that email. Schulte: So that's over-reaching. Let's go to 1062. Mr. Weber is escalating the issue directly to you, correct? Leonis: I'm in his management chain.

Schulte: You never asked me my side of the story, right? CIA's Leonis: I needed more information -

Schulte: I'm sorry, sir, just answer yes or no. Leonis: No.

Schulte: You could have called a meeting between us and resolved it? Leonis: I needed info first.

CIA's Leonis: My concern was who had admin privileges to the libraries. Schulte: What does that entail? Leonis: Control over the libraries. Being able to change or modify things. Schulte: But you also said everyone has the ability to do that, to write code

Schulte: So on April 18 you begin to write the memo of warning, right? CIA Leonis: No. Schulte: You didn't? Leonis: It was a memorandum. Schulte: You wrote it without even speaking with me, right?

Leonis: We were going to talk with you about it. Schulte: The question is, you had decided on April 18 you were going to issue me the memorandum? Leonis: Yes. But then we were going to have a conversation.

Schulte: But H.R. wasn't even there, right? CIA Leonis: I think they were there. Schulte: But they didn't sign the memorandum as a witness. Aren't they supposed to sign the memo? AUSA: Objection. Judge Furman: Sustained.

Schulte: Did you know that the Atlassian tools were installed by Patrick? AUSA: Objection! Judge Furman: Sustained.

Schulte: This cut-off had only to do with Atlassian, and no other servers like IRC, right? AUSA: Objection. Judge Furman: Sustained. It speaks for itself, Mr. Schulte.

Schulte: Are you aware of Dave D. who worked in RDB? CIA's Leonis: I don't know how to answer your question.

Schulte: Uh, with yes or no? Leonis: I'm aware of a Dave. Schulte: And he moved. Leonis: Yes.

Judge Furman: OK, jurors, we'll take our break now. Do not discuss the case. And Mr. Leonis, you remain on cross examination, do not discuss it with the government. [Later]

Jury entering!

Judge Furman: You may proceed. Schulte: Good afternoon. Before testifying, you met with AUSA Denton 15 times, correct?

CIA's Leonis: Less. Maybe 10. Schulte: Some lasted several hours, right? Leonis: Maybe two hours.

Schulte: Brutal Kangaroo is the project, right? CIA's Leonis: It is the tool suite.

Schulte: Shattered Assurance is one of the tools, and uses Drifting Deadline, right? Leonis: That's what it says here. Judge Furman: I think we've covered this.

Schulte: Let's talk about Weekly Activity Reports. Did I submit mine to you? Leonis: Yes. Schulte: I'd like to read this --

Judge Furman: Don't. It's in evidence. Move on. [With jury out of room, Judge Furman urged Schulte to finish his cross of Leonis today

Leonis: Shattered Assurance was inside Brutal Kangaroo. It was your job to --

Schulte: I object, Judge.

Judge Furman: Overruled. Schulte: I move to introduce the stipulation 3008. Judge Furman: You don't have to read the first paragraph.

Judge Furman: I'm giving you fifteen or twenty minutes more. Schulte: Can we have a sidebar? Judge Furman: No. Let's do it more quickly please.

Schulte: I want to talk about the 'fight back' statement. Is there not a formal way for CIA employees to fight back?

CIA Leonis: Fight back is not language we use. But there are mechanisms to address concerns. Schulte: Did you know that through the CIA's formal process my performance report (PAR) was modified? Leonis: No.

Schulte: How do you characterize my demeanor at the meeting? Leonis: You were frustrated. Schulte: When was the first time you talked to me about access to Brutal Kangaroo? Leonis: We said, all projects. Schulte: But project were transferred with me.

CIA Leonis: You were told which projects would could take with you. Schulte: It never said Brutal Kangaroo. Judge Furman: Mr. Schulte, you may not testify. Put on your mask and let me see counsel at sidebar.

[After long sidebar] Schulte: OK I want to talk about security. Did you know that the CCI site was an SC Zero cite?

AUSA: Objection. Judge Furman: Just yes or no. CIA's Leonis: Yes. Schulte: And what does that mean? AUSA: Objection. Judge Furman: Sustained.

Schulte: The CIA interviews and tests applicant there, right? CIA's Leonis: I don't know.

AUSA: Your Honor we are getting into the issue that came up the other day. Schulte: May stand-by counsel hand a copy -- AUSA: We object! Judge Furman: At the sidebar again.

[Back up] Schulte: I want to ask you about DEVLAN. Have you heard it described as the Wild, Wild West?

CIA's Leonis: No. Never heard that. Schulte: Did you know that a developer put the Stash backup on a public page? Leonis: No.

Schulte: Is it CIA policy to basically close up shop after a leak? AUSA: Objection. Judge Furman: Sustained. Let's wrap this up. Schulte: Are you aware of the Wikileaks task force? CIA's Leonis: Yes. But I was not party to it.

Schulte: No further questions. Judge Furman: Any re-direct? AUSA: No, Your Honor. Judge Furman: Mr. Leonis you are free to go. Have a nice weekend.

XI.

The day after Juneteenth (observed) the Joshua Schulte trial continued. On the stand was Patrick Leedom of Microsoft, but before that the MITRE group, They worked with the FBI to investigate who leaked Vault 7.

On direct Leedom said Schulte was quickly suspect number 1, with strange logs in and the deletion of log files. When, with an hour left in the trial day, Schule got his chance to cross examine, he asked Leedom who paid for his hotel and taxis, and if there weren't others more qualified that him to investigate cyber tools.

These triggered objections, mostly sustained. Schulte soldiered on, saying he might have to bring in a confidential document for the cross, which would only resume Friday. No explanation of the two days off was given.

Kurt Wheelock had heard other judges talking about an upcoming Judicial Conference. And Judge Furman now said the trial would likely run to or past July 10. The alternate juror who needed to fly to Oregon for a dress-fitting could be let go, he said. But what about another, who wanted or needed July 5? Schulte was led out, and then to the MDC. Kurt Wheelock went to cover two other trial in the courthouse, one drugs, the other fake loans for cars. The wheels of justice turned slowly.

XII.

During the days off that interspersed the trial, Kurt Wheelock was reading up on Wikileaks and higher profile leakers Edward Snowden and Chelsea Manning. Many viewed them as heroes - Kurt checked out an audio book - but few portrayed Schulte that way. Was it because he denied it?

Chelsea Manning too, was said to have mixed motives.

Kurt remembered what he was still in the UN before they threw him out, correspondents who cared nothing about press freedom nevertheless asking about Julian Assange. It was a perfect crutch for the UN - a few cryptic statements by a special rapporteur, and the whole UN system could ask in the glow.

The US administration, now being lobbied to stop trying to extradite Assange, didn't see or want to see how the UN was playing them, for China and others. Maybe, as in the story Kurt was writing, all of the P5 worked together. The Five that spy together, lie together.

Interlude: Some History of Wikileaks - and at the UN:

When Wikileaks smashed Kenya's Daniel Arap Moi for corruption, Kurt Wheelock had just arrived at the United Nations. It was an organization intent on covering up or silencing coverage of its own corruption, while pointing its finger at others.

It was before the global predatory lending meltdown, which Kurt after facing legal threats from JPMorgan Chase and Citigroup observed on an analog television set raised up near the ceiling of the marble hallway outside the clubhouse of the UN Correspondents Association, another corrupt organization.

In that crisis, Wikileaks found juice in the lava fields of Iceland, stepping in when the national broadcaster there was told to stand silent. The UN, meanwhile, bluewashed the Wall Street predators as environmental heroes, even as they continued to fund mountain-top removal coal mining.

That had been how Kurt began at the UN: at a conference about banks and the environment, held in the mausoleum of the UN's Trusteeship Chamber. From deep in the cheap seats he'd pushed the microphone button and asked a question, about CitiFinancial and predatory lending, and Deutsche Bank's securitizing of it. Both were been given awards at the UN that day.

After the question was dodged from the podium, the audience was told to go buy lunch either in the UN cafeteria on the first floor, or the Delegates Dining Room on the fourth, while the organizers held a press conference.

It was to that that Kurt went, or tried to go. But as he looked in through the smoked glass door of the

UN Press Briefing Room, he was told that it was only for UN accredited journalists.

But I have a blog, Kurt said. Inner City Press dot org.

The UN's media man Gary Fowlie shook his head. Dot org? That makes you an NGO. This is for real journalists.

Kurt thought about it. But isn't Associated Press a dot org? And National Public Radio?

Whatever, Fowlie said. You can't go in.

Kurt stood in the hall, looking and listening through the glass door. Inside an UNCA correspondent asked, But tell me, why is Bank of America so deeply committed to the environment?

Why indeed.

The next day Kurt returned to the UN, paying money to enter as a tourist and going up to the Media Acceditation and Liaison Unit. He had purchased the Inner City Press dot com domain name, and thrown up a couple of stories.

It worked. They provisionally accredited him for three months. "We'll see if the other correspondents accept you. They do not want to be lobbied by some NGO in their midst," he was told.

"Don't worry," Kurt said. "I'm not here to hand stories over to corporate media. I'm here to get scoops and leaks." That word again. And so it began.

* * *

Flashback to Kenya, where Kroll Associated had been paid to investigate the thefts by Daniel Arap Moi. The report had been finished in 2004, long before Kurt showed up at the UN. But it didn't come up until 2006, when Wikileaks got it and gave it to the Guardian.

Kenyan TV at the time sourced the whole thing to the Guardian. No one knew that this middleman Wikileaks was not like other middlemen, or wouldn't long be. A parliamentarian / poet in Iceland joined up with them, and an Icelandic bank was brought low.

Later Wikileaks said it was preparing a huge leak about an American bank. Had it happened? Kurt felt if it had, he would have remembered. It was something he would look into.

Back in court:

OK - it's US v Josh Schulte trial, Day 5.

Judge Furman: Jurors, welcome back. Government, you may proceed.

Assistant US Attorney: Good morning. Remind us, what did Mr Schulte do?

Microsoft's Patrick Leedom: He reverted to an earlier date. Then I investigated the network. The FBI was making forensic images

AUSA: How did you come to focus on Mr. Schulte? Leedom: It all starting point back to him. When we reviewed his machines and his logs, we found some very suspicious things. AUSA: Let's put up the chart and compare what #Wikileaks published to Mr. Schulte's logs

AUSA: What's the difference between a desktop and a server? Microsoft's Leedom: A server is in a rack. It is basically like a beefy desktop.

AUSA: What type operating system ran on DevLAN? Leedom: Window, Mac OS and Linux. AUSA: We offer this chart of DevLAN into evidence. Judge Furman: Any objection? Schulte: No objection.

AUSA: At the risk as asking the obvious, what is "Date Created"? [Jurors look bored - which happened during the first trial, too. This could take a while - but Schulte's own cross-examination of Microsoft's Leedom should be something]. Thread continues...

AUSA: Did you review what Wikileaks published? Leedom: I did, the actual web pages. AUSA: Where did the March 7 leak come from? Leedom: The March 3 Confluence back-up. AUSA: How do you know? Leedom: The command was missing an argument.

AUSA: Let's look at what was posted on #Wikileaks. What is this? Leedom: A page from the #Vault7 release. AUSA: Did it appear as it would have on Confluence on DevLAN? Leedom: Yes.

Leedom: Wikileaks has its own font and color, but that's superficial. The information is the same. I didn't go though the page relationship or navigation directory. AUSA: What conclusions did you draw? Leedom: It made it easier to figure out how they stole it.

Leedom: We know this "165" is Schulte's workstation. Here, he requests administrative access to OLB Libraries, as SchulJo AUSA: Does some person have to take an action to generate the event? Leedom: Since he had the permissions, it was automatic. Judge Furman: Mr Denton, would this be a natural place to stop?

AUSA Denton: Yes, your Honor. Judge Furman: OK, jurors, we'll take our break. Enjoy it. [Jury leaves] AUSA Denton: We may finish direct today. We are 2 days behind. [Oh, that pesky cross-examination]

Schulte: I want to note depending on how the government, once they get a chance to look at the letter I sent them, there may be a need to introduce the classified exhibit on cross. Judge Furman: That's not happening this afternoon. [Thread will continue]

[They're back] AUSA: Did this session by Mr. Schulte eventually end? Leedom: Yes, he logged out at 1:47. AUSA: Do you see where he said "all private keys have been destroyed"? Leedom: Yes. But he was still using them.

AUSA: Any activity with regard to the March 3 back up? Leedom: Yes, they were accessed on April 20. Then he as administrator deleted log files-not normal.

Judge Furman: Could you just explain the basis for that testimony? Leedom: Only delete when out of space.

Leedom: Having worked on cases where people nefariously hack in -- Schulte: Objection! Judge Furman: Overruled.

AUSA: Did the defendant revert to that snapshot right away? Leedom: He had to create a new one first. But eventually yes. A client on his work station was used to make this, at 5:29 pm on April 20.

Leedom: It's my opinion that these files were copied by the defendant. AUSA: How do you know this? Leedom: Wikileaks published these exact files. Schulte: Objection! Judge Furman: Overruled.

Leedom: It seems Mr. Schulte was using a scorched earth approach, just deleting all the log files and not just the juicy ones. AUSA: What do you conclude? Leedom: That the log deletions were successful.

AUSA: No further questions. Judge Furman: Cross examination. Schulte: Hello. Slide 89 - these are your forensic findings, correct? Leedom: Yes.

Schulte: You state in bullet 1, "Schulte used" - but in bullet 2 you just say they were accessed, right? Leedom: Yes.

Schulte: These were based on logs you retrieved from my CIA work station, right? Leedom: Yes. Schulte: But my work station would have not been impacted from the reversion, right? Leedom: I don't understand.

Schulte: You met with the prosecutors to prepare, right? Leedom: Yes. Schulte: It was flattering to be picked to work on the case? Leedom: It was.

Schulte: Raise your profile in the MITRE Corporation? Leedom: In some ways. Schulte: Now you're at Microsoft. A: Yes Schulte: DOJ is paying for your hotel? Leedom: Yes. Schulte: You had lunch with the prosecutors?

Leedom (laughs) Yes I did. Schulte: You prepared your slides with Mr. Denton? Leedom: Yes I did. Schulte: You had complete access to the DevLAN machines, right? Leedom: Yes. Schulte: But you didn't recognize many of the CIA tools, right?

Leedom: Right. Schulte: So someone else would have been more qualified -- AUSA: Objection! Judge Furman: Sustained.

Schulte: Do you recall that the government said it must have happened on March 7? Leedom: I'm a little blurry on that. Schulte: Where did the FBI get that date?

Leedom: I don't remember. Schulte: Were you involved in that analysis? Leedom: I was in transition.

Schulte: Did you review the security of DevLAN? Leedom: Yes. Schulte: How was its security? Leedom: Below average. Schulte: Did you research the permission to access Stash? Leedom: I didn't really work on that specifically.

****

Schulte: Did you know that Stuxnet was all over DevLAN?

AUSA: Objection! Can we have a sidebar?

Judge Furman: The objection is sustained.

****

Schulte: Would they know if someone just downloaded information onto a thumb drive? Leedom: I don't know. I can't speak to that. Judge Furman: This is where we'll call it for the day - until Friday. Don't discuss the case.

[Jury leaves] Judge Furman: Mr Leedom, sorry you'll be here longer. But you're being compensated. You are excused. [Leedom leaves]

Judge Furman: Mr Schulte came close to saying he wasn't given any forensic images. Is a curative instruction needed? AUSA: If/when.

AUSA: There is a problem with Mr. Schulte saying, "Were you aware" - it's like he's testifying.

Judge Furman: Ask more neutrally. Given the pace, I think we'll run to or past July 10. Adjourned.

* * *

Unlike Schulte with his halting cross examinations often ended or pausing in "Okay" when Judge Furman shut him down, Edward Snowden or at least his audio book reader was self-assured. That didn't mean Ed was always right. Kurt was listening to Chapter 15, riding a stationary bike and lifting weights in the housing project gym, when Snowdon asserted that Geneva was the global headquarters of the United Nations - maybe, if you meant, HQ for the rest of the world - and then, glaringly, that it was the headquarters of the International Atomic Energy Agency.

No, that would be Vienna. So what else was wrong in the book? Snowden mentioned getting an infected thumb drive designed by the CIA to put into computers in the UN in Geneva. Had that been a Schulte-designed thumb drive? With Brutal Kangaroo?

XIII.

During the two day lull in the Josh Schulte trial, Kurt Wheelock while running between cases of judges who hadn't gone to the Judicial Conference found himself thinking, what made Schulte different than Chelsea Manning or Edward Snowden?

The latter had written a memoir while still in Russia, portraying himself as serving the public and no longer the government.

Manning was celebrated, at least on the margins, as an outsider truthteller, somehow like Virginia Woolf, Bayard Rustin and even Michel Foucault. But Schulte? He was presented as just a resentful troll. So far his cross examination did little to counter that. Kurt found himself being accused of being pro Schulte. It was only because others were so anti-Schulte.

Between cases as Kurt walked across the eighth floor of the courthouse, to the side elevator bank he had trailed others to from the Patrick Ho trial after he'd been thrown out of the UN, not knowing where it lead - he saw Schulte's lawyer, or stand-by counsel.

He waved but didn't stop to talk. After his experience at the UN, he found himself staying above the fray, asking for nothing, just glad to be there to report. And report he would - the trial was restarting.

XIV.

When the Joshua Schulte trial resumed on June 24, he'd had two more days to prepare, in the Metropolitan Detention Center in Brooklyn and the SCIF on the ninth floor of the courthouse. But so had the witness, Microsoft's Patrick Leedom, in better conditions. Leedom smirking on the witness state repeated said, I disagree. The Assist US Attorney cut in with "Objection," leading nine times out of ten to "Sustained... Move it along, Mr. Schulte, or I'll have to shut you down."

Kurt Wheelock was sitting in the front row, just behind Schulte. When he'd come into the courtroom that was the only row empty. Schulte's parents were in the second row; FBI agent Michael Berger, an expert witness who would testify next, was in the gallery listening to Leedom.

Schulte had two laptops along with the monitor that came with rostrum. He had Post-It notes from his stand-by counsel and, it seemed to Kurt, a few white or grey hairs in his beard. His hands were thin, and his nails were not cut short. When he laughed, it sounded forced: Ha. Ha.

In the back from of the jury box, one of the alternate jurors was outright sleeping. Kurt kept wondering if Judge Furman would notice and say nothing. How could his man deliberated, if he hadn't heard all the testimony? Maybe it wouldn't come to that. But maybe it would.

More:

Ok- US v Schulte trial Day 6, Schulte crossing Microsoft's Leedom, courtroom thread

Schulte at podium 5 feet from Juror 6, with 2 laptops, Post-It notes from stand by counsel. On exhibits screen: "Palo Alto Firewall" from HICKOK server.

Schulte: Do you have a contact in #Wikileaks? AUSA: Objection! Judge Furman: Sustained.

Schulte: Both friendly and unfriendly nations run cyber operations against each other, right? AUSA: Objection! Judge: Overruled. Leedom: I can't really speak to foreign policy.

NOTE: An alternate juror is sleeping Inner City Press @innercitypress · 3h Schulte zeroing in on mysqldump command. Leedom: This is a hypothetical scenario.

OK - they've back from break and more (frequent) live tweeting: [Judge Furman told Schulte to speed it up or he will shut him down] Schulte: You know working at the CIA is not a 9 to 5 job, right? Microsoft's Leedom: Right

Schulte: I move to introduce this exhibit, 1207... AUSA: Objection! Judge Furman: Sustained. Schulte: Ok. This script command is the one that generates files like these, right? AUSA: Objection. Judge: Sustained.

Judge Furman: Can I see the parties at sidebar? Jurors, you can use this time to stretch. [After sidebar:] Schulte: You testified I deleted log files on the ESXI server, correct? Leedom: Correct. Schulte: No further questions at this time (1:48 pm)

Judge Furman: Re-direct. ASUA: Mr. Schulte asked you if material had been deleted from his CIA work station and you referred to a host? Leedom: Yes, his DevLan, using Windows with a virtual machine.

Judge Furman: Mr. Denton, next witness. AUSA Denton: The government calls Michael Berger.... Who do you work for? Berger: For the FBI. As a computer scientist. I have a masters in computer forensics. I teach digital forensics at NYU.

AUSA Denton: Are you familiar with the FBI's CAT team? Berger: I'm a member the CAT, the Cyber Action Team. [Berger is qualified as an expert; Schulte does not object] AUSA: Did you work in the investigation into the Vault 7 leak to Wikileaks? Berger: Yes.

AUSA: Did Wikileaks suggesting using TOR to leak to it? Berger: Yes. AUSA: Did you find that Mr. Schulte used TOR? Berger: Yes, on a virtual machine in his apartment. Judge Furman: We'll break there for the week. Jurors, don't discuss the case. Keep an open mind. [Jury leaves]

Judge: Now much more direct with Mr. Berger? AUSA: An hour and a half. Judge: Mr. Schulte, some of your cross got bogged down, lost on the jury.

Judge Furman: Using the witness to get hearsay in front of the jury is not fair game. Now we'll reconvene in classified setting -- AUSA: Ask the defendant about his control of his own defense. Judge Furman: Do you control your defense? Schulte: Yes.

Schulte: I got the US letter about the defense witnesses yesterday in the SCIF, the Marshals let me stay until 5. I need time.

Judge Furman: You can be transported to and from the SCIF and we reconvene at 3:45.

XV.

As Josh Schulte plodded on with his cross examination, today of FBI agent Michael Berger, it became a surreal way of testifying. Schulte asked

Berger, did you know that I often played League of Legends the video game until 4 am?

Berger deadpanned, That wasn't part of my forensic investigation. But he had to admit a few times they had not direct evidence that Schulte was the source of the leak to Wikileaks.

Next up would be Jeremy Weber, and Schulte told Judge Furman he might have to ask Weber about the "bartender" tool that appeared in Schulte's prison writings and for which he was charged. Kurt Wheelock perked up - now things might get back into the nerf gun battles that features so prominently in the first trial, and seemed to have led to the mistrial.

The Assistant US Attorney during an absence of the jurors - one of whom already had come down with COVID - complained to Judge Furman about the length of Schulte's cross examinations, how they now couldn't be able to close by the end of this the third week of trial.

Then would come Schulte's witnesses, however many Judge Furman might allow. Wheelock was still hoping for Mike Pompeo. There was something about Wikileaks.

On June 27, FBI agent Michael Berger was cross examined, thread here:

Ok- US v Joshua Schulte trial Day 7, Assistant US Attorney still questioning FBI's Michael Berger seeking to link the Vault 7 transfer to Wikileaks to Schulte.

AUSA: Do you recall the size of the Confluence back up in March of 2016? Berger: Tens of gigabytes. AUSA: Look at Page 93 of GX 1704. What is this use for? Berger: It's a utility to securely erase files.

AUSA: So here you can see the defendant -- Schulte: Objection - leading. Judge Furman: Fair point but I'll allow it. AUSA: At what time was the virtual screen saver unlocked? Berger: 3:15 am.Cross examination: Schulte: Let's talk about the hard drive found at my home. FBI Agent Berger: Ok.

Schulte: You didn't find any CIA drives in my home, did you? FBI Agent Berger: I don't know.

Schulte: You didn't take the drives from my home and compare them to CIA numbers? Berger: I didn't personally do that. I can't say one way or another. Schulte: Similarly you found my evidence that my hard drives were ever connected to CIA computers, right? A: No.

Schulte: Is it conceivable that Wikileaks could track these versions from a much later backup? FBI's Berger: In order to only disclose some of the data? Is that what you're asking? They would need to have a copy of the March 3 data base.

Schulte: I wrote malware for the CIA, right? FBI Berger: Yes. Schulte: Including LINUX malware, right? FBI Berger: I don't know. Schulte: Wouldn't that be important, with what you've said about my Google searches?

AUSA: Objection! Judge Furman: Ask a new question Schulte: So you familiarized yourself with Wikileaks, right? FBI's Berger: Yes.

Schulte: And you became aware Wikileaks tries to help people providing information to them to conceal their identities, right? AUSA: Objection! Judge Furman: Overruled.

Schulte: I used the Plex service, allowing uploading of videos by many users, right? FBI's Berger: I was not aware.

Schulte: You testified about wiping a computer, right? A: Yes. There were files on your D-drive.

Schulte: Couldn't it have been an upgrade? A: Yes. Judge Furman: Jurors, we'll take our break. [Jury exits]

Judge Fruman: Who will be the next witness? AUSA: Jeremy Weber. Judge Furman: Ok, we'll see you back here. Thread will continue.

They're back - and Schulte is cross examining FBI's Berger about his Amazon purchases.

Schulte: So beyond the pillow cases & pancake maker, there was a docking station, correct? Berger: Yes. Schulte: We see the same device purchased again, right? Berger: Seems so.

 Schulte: In your presentation you wanted to imply that my docking station was used to transmit info, right?

AUSA: Objection! Judge Furman: Sustained. Schulte: Okay. Judge Furman: Can I see the parties at the sidebar? [Note: for the next witness, Jeremy Weber, Judge Furman has said the sealed courtroom procedures will be implemented, with people asked to leave, including the jury for a moment so they are not told it's sealed]

Schulte: You never found Brutal Kangaroo on my home computers, right? FBI's Berger: We did not.

Schulte: Solid state drivers would be wiped differently than other drives, correct? Berger: Yes.

Schulte: Here, I was playing League of Legends, right? FBI's Berger: Yes. Schulte: And that's a video game, correct? FBI Berger: It is.

Schulte: Did you find that I stayed up late often playing League of Legends? FBI Berger: That was not part of my investigation.

Schulte: There is no evidence I transferred anything to Wikileaks, right? FBI's Berger: Incorrect. The evidence that information was transferred to Wikileaks is the fact that they published it.

Schulte (laughs) - But that is not evidence that I transferred it.

Judge Furman: I suggest we move to re-direct while you fix your technical issues, Mr. Schulte. AUSA: Mr. Berger, what type of forensic artifacts would be relevent -

Schulte: Objection! Form! AUSA: Let me rephrase. AUSA: What would happen if you removed files from the Ray 5 Array?

FBI's Berger: The data would be recoverable. But not from a single drive. AUSA: You were asked about Google Search history- Schulte: Objection! Judge Furman: Overruled.

 AUSA: Mr. Berger, who conducted the activity that prevented your ability to reconstruct -- Schulte: Objection.

Judge Furman: Sustained. Any brief re-cross? [It's 2:43]

 Schulte: You found no artifacts of Tails, right? Berger: It was all wiped.

Schulte: You testified that the Wikileaks URL was needed to access to TOR service, right? FBI's Berger: Yes, through dot onion. Schulte: But you'd have to use the regular Internet, right? Berger: Someone could tell you what it is.

 Schulte: You said this was wiped and re-formatted, right? FBI's Berger: I said that's my opinion? Schulte: But it could have just been completely new, yes? Berger: It's possible.

 Schulte: You noted the time of April 18, 2016, correct? FBI's Berger: I'm not sure what you mean.

Judge Furman: Mr. Schulte, we are on borrowed time. Schulte: No further questions. But wait there's more - after jury leaves, Judge Furman mentioned the possibility of compensating juror(s) for changes travel plans given trial already going on. Schulte: I got a video from the UN on June 14. It's prejudicial. AUSA: It replaces a prior version.

AUSA: It was shown at the prior trial. It's just higher quality. Schulte: It doesn't show me doing anything. It just shows me in prison. AUSA: I don't recall the specifics of the video. We'll take a second look at it.

Schulte: The next witness, Weber, I may go long on the cross because it would lessen my need for the other witnesses I've called. Judge Furman: The next witness will be subject to the courtroom closure procedures.

Schulte: GX 806 page 2, part of the notebook was redacted, it was intended for Judge Crotty. I wrote: There's been no reason over the past year we do not have access -- AUSA: We will object. He's saying the prosecutors lied. Judge Furman: I'd like to review it.

Schulte: With this next witness I may need to reference Classified Exhibit 1. Judge Furman: If you are asking to display it, we've litigated that, it's not necessary. Schulte: The pages about the bar tender, I'd like to reference it with the witness.

Judge Furman: That ship has sailed. It is only admitted as a classified exhibit not to be discussed in the courtroom. So you're not doing it. Schulte. Okay... The IRC chats, they were not admitted with years, so it's misleading.

AUSA: If Mr. Schulte intends to call himself as his expert, he had to provide notice. And he hasn't. Judge Furman: I have not had the opportunity to research that legal question, but I would be surprised if that were not the law.

Judge Furman: OK, we are finished for the day. See you tomorrow.

XVI.

Listening to Schulte go around and around in circles, between getting slapped down by Judge Furman, was beginning to depress Kurt Wheelock. He was forgoing other cases he was supposed to cover, for example the fake electric truck trial of Trevor Milton of Nikola, for which a trade publication said it would pay him for coverage. Kurt was all-in on Schulte. But where was it headed?

At the end of the trial date Kurt would head out of the courthouse's Pearl Street exit and walk by Chatham Green and One Police Plaza, listening now to an audio book recording of Edward Snowden's "Permanent Record." Snowden portrayed himself a cool hacker, and video game player. Why was Schulte so uncool? Why was in the MDC rather than in exile?

Kurt turned back into Wikileaks, all the way back to the Kenya leaks, and the Iceland banks. Manning in Iraq, Collateral Murder and the role of Adrian Lamo. But where were Schulte's defenders? Kurt struggled to fill the void.

XVII.

The CIA witness they called Jeremy Weber was in the witness box in the semi sealed courtroom. There was no feed in the Press Room - today was Ghislaine Maxwell's sentencing day, Maximum Maxwell - and, strangely, the docket in the morning showed that the trial was continued to the next day, June 29.

But when Kurt ran up to the overflow courtroom, the trial was being shown on the screen. There was no one else there but for a Court Security Officer. Another had asked, Why aren't you covering Maxwell? Or, only covering Maxwell?

Once after four hours Judge Nathan dropped her twenty years on Ghislaine, Kurt ran up to the courtroom itself. There were two CSOs outside.

"Is it still sealed?" Kurt asked.

Yes, was the answer. Kurt remembered the two pool reporter provision he'd won, and had been using. "I guess you can go in," one of the CSOs said. "You could have just told us."

"Sorry," Kurt said. He hadn't been thinking straight. In the second row were Schulte's parents and a younger man, maybe a brother.

"How much more cross do you have?" Judge Furman asked Schulte.

"Maybe ten more pages," Schulte replied.

"How many pages have you gone through so far?" the judge asked.

Schulte flipped through his binder, that he carried with him up to the ninth floor SCIF, and apparently in the van back to the MDC in

Brooklyn, where he said he'd wait for hours to get readmitted. The most exclusive ticket in town. "Fifty," he finally said. "So I'm five sixths through."

"Good," Judge Furman said. "We're going to need to streamline things." It was all being streamlined. There was almost nobody here. Why?

Sealed

On June 28, Day 8, the courtroom went sealed again, and without at least one of the feeds that was supposed to exist. Inside, "Jeremy Weber" was being cross-examined by Schulte. At day's end Schulte told Judge Furman he has ten more pages of questions for Weber, after finishing with 50 pages.

XVIII.

With the Ghislaine Maxwell sentencing day coming up, Kurt had tried to suggest that while three of the four screens in the Press Room be Maximum Maxwell, the small screen on the side be for the Schulte trial, since the feed was provided for in Judge Furman's courtroom sealing order.

But when Kurt got in that morning, all four screens were on Maxwell. He thought it better not to complain, remembering as always where that had led at the UN. If he complained and nothing was done, he escalated and the next thing you knew.... out on the street, ranting at a TV screen. Not this time.

Still, how to cover the Schulte trial and also live tweet the passion of Ghislaine? In actuality she was not passionate at all, a carefully modulated pseudo-apology, noting the pain of the victims without taking responsibility. Well, she'd be appealing.

The sentencing ran almost to 2:45 pm and Kurt almost didn't go upstairs. But he did, and got into the courtroom, saw the brother and was seen. The father looked him over. Judge Furman had another proceeding coming up and his deputy told Schulte's lawyers to be sure to clear off the table for the in-custody defendant who would be brought in from the holding cell.

While Foley Square was full of TV trucks for Ghislaine the pedophile, there was nobody up here for Schulte. How different it would have been for Snowden, who'd told Trevor Noah that he would return to the US from Moscow if he could be guaranteed a fair trial, in which he could use all evidence.

Here, Schulte was not allowed to use some exhibits, at least not in open court, or even ask questions about them. Could a trial like this be fair? Then again, how was the government to prosecute a leaker? Were all leakers whistleblowers? Were some just destructive?

Some people celebrated Manning, for asserting the rights of the different by making a world-historical data dump to Wikileaks. But the messages with Adrian Lamo led to a fait accompli in the military legal system. So this might be the only non-military trial. And there was hardly anyone here. Kurt decided he should double down. But how?

XIX.

For the CIA witnesses, even just the paper-pushers, the courtroom was sealed in the Joshua Schulte trial. But when Carlos Betances from the Dominican Republic by way of the MCC was the witness, the courtroom was re-opened. Not that many people went.

Kurt was there as Betances on direct said that he lived in Rockland County. Why then was he in a prison uniform? He described getting phones for not only Schulte but also Omar Anamat, scammer and first cousin of Huma Abadeen. The political echoes were everywhere, Kurt thought. At least Maurene Comey wasn't prosecuting this case.

Betances was being held, and not deported, to squeeze everything they could out of him as a cooperator. Now that two jurors had been knocked out of the Schulte case due to COVID, the possibility of a second mistrial this time on virus grounds arose. Would they keep Carlos on ice for a third trial? The US would never let Schulte go.

Meanwhile Reality Winner, who pleaded guilty to leaking NSA intelligence about Russian interference in election, was asking the Administration for a pardon. If convicted on the CIA counts, or even now with only lying to the FBI and the pending sex charges, Schulte would never get a pardon. They'd left him no option. He pressed forward with cross examination, in an emptying courthouse with a shrinking jury. And the blogger would remains. More here on Patreon.

Had Josh Schulte been treated fairly in his big write-up? Was anyone, ever? The piece has strongly implied that he was guilty, and unlike Snowden there was no high minded rationale offered or allowed. Schulte was angry at Amol, the story went, he was angry at a lack of women, despite his 39th Street apartment and $200,000 a year job at Bloomberg LP on Park Avenue. Why hadn't he run, like Snowden did? Or move into an embassy? But which one would take him?

Kurt before being thrown out of the UN had been invited to receptions at countries' ambassadors' residences, like the mansion of the Japanese, with unlimited sushi. Once near the end he'd crashed an event of the French Ambassador, just after publishing leaked information about their colonialism in Ivory Coast.

"If you don't leave we'll call the police," the French Mission spokesman had hissed at Kurt. He'd waiting, until the last minute, then left. But they would get their revenge. At least he was still walking around free. He reminded himself of that.

And as he covered the Schulte retrial, just before the Fourth of July break, he decided to dig into a particular connection. Carlos Betances had testified about getting phones for not only Schulte but also Omar Anamat, Twilight scammer and first cousin of Huma Abadeen. What were the connection? Kurt dug in.

Back in court:

OK - US v. Josh Schulte trial, Day 9 starts with a second juror out with COVID. Judge Furman says they'll plow forward but that it's reaching the point no more jurors can be excused or lost. Weber still on stand. Cross examination continues.

Schulte: Fair to say that be the time I complained about Amol, you had stopped liking me?

Weber: I was tired of the drama. Schulte: You were talking to Amol, right? Weber: I think Amol went on vacation.

Schulte: At some point you spoke in court for Amol, right? Weber: I did. Schulte: And you went out for a beer with him, correct? Weber: I don't recall. Schulte: I refer you to page 6. Read it to yourself. Weber: I have a vague recollection of it.

Schulte: You are aware that Amol later admitted to the allegations, right? Weber: I am not aware of that. Schulte: You were aware Amol was struggling with multiple other personal issues, right?

AUSA: Objection! Judge Furman: Sustained

Schulte: You are aware that there had recently been a shooting incident at a Navy base, right? Let's move on to the cutting off of my access. You cut me off without sending me an e-mail right? Weber: Yes. Schulte: The policy was to send an email, right? Weber: No.

Schulte: And you also didn't tell me face to face, right? Weber: Correct. Schulte: If you didn't tell me my access had been cut off, how was I supposed to know? Weber: I wasn't thinking about that.

Schulte: So you changed me from Write to Read on Brutal Kangaroo, right? Weber: I did. Schulte: And Shattered Assurance too, correct? Weber: Yes.

Schulte: You would agree I am very litigious, right? AUSA: Objection! Judge Furman: Sustained. Schulte: I challenged my Performance Review, right? AUSA: Objection. Judge Furman: Overruled.

Schulte: To your knowledge I always advocated my position by legal means, correct? AUSA: Objection. Judge Furman: Yes. Schulte: I had no security violations, right? Weber: You plugged a thumb drive into a computer that wasn't supposed to have one.

Schulte: But that was when I was an intern, right? Weber: I believe so. Schulte: No further questions. Thread will continue.

AUSA: Did they come a time when the CIA made a criminal referral? Witness: Yes. AUSA: What effect did that referral have? Witness: The investigation was by the FBI, walled off. AUSA: Any relationship with the Wikileaks Task Force? Witness: It was walled off.

Cross examination. Schulte: This email was the first time you ever heard of me? Witness: Correct. Schulte: Before this you had not had any conversation with Karen, right? Witness: Yes. Schulte: Where were you when you got this email? Witness: In my office.

Next witness will be in Spanish. Judge Furman tells jurors to rely only on the English translation, even if they speak Spanish. Vamos a ver.

AUSA: Where do you live?

Witness Carlos Betances: Rockland County.

AUSA: Where you arrested in 2018?

Betances: Yes, in the Bronx. AUSA: Were you in the MCC? Betances: Yes, in March 2018. AUSA:

Do you see anyone who was in with you?
Betances: Yes. Josh.

AUSA: Where is Josh sitting? Betances: Between the two ladies. AUSA: Have you pled guilty to crimes? Betances: Yes - drug, mail fraud, entering the country illegal. AUSA: And ID theft? Betances: Yes. AUSA: And contraband in jail? Betances: Yes.

AUSA: Did the defendant ask for your help with cell phones? Betances: Yes. It was Omar [Amanat], Chino, him and me. They asked me for help to bring the phone in. [Inner City Press covered the Omar Amanat case, here

AUSA: When did you start taking photos in the MCC? Betances: I was watching to make sure guard weren't coming. I overheard Josh... AUSA: Did Josh, Chino and Omar know you were taking the pictures? Betances: No. AUSA: Who used the Samsung phone? Betances: Josh. He said there were things he could do better on a Samsung than on an iPhone. Judge Furman: It's 2:45 and we'll leave it here for the day. [Jury exits]

Schulte: The government can't have its cake and eat it too.

Schulte: We tried to get it declassified, they said no. But then they ask about it. They can't have it both ways. Judge Furman: Mr. Denton? AUSA: No one identified the tool or the vendor. Judge Furman: But you asked, are you familiar with the vendor referred to

Judge Furman: There has been some slippage - I remind the parties I would like to begin on time tomorrow. [This is not an issue for Schulte: he is transported from the MDC by the Marshals] Adjourned.

XX.

After Josh Schulte established, at length, that the cooperator against him Carlos Betances had sold drugs in the Bronx and was testifying not only to shorten his sentence but also to try to get an S visa to stay in the United States, things moved to FBI Agent Evan Schlessinger.

He had led a team of 50, yes Five-Oh, agents into the MCC jail in 2018 to search for Schulte's cell phone that Chirping Carlos had smuggled in then told the prosecutors and FBI, through his lawyer, about.

That the phone was also used by Omar Amanat, the first cousin of Huma Abadeen, didn't matter to him he said. They knew what they were looking for. And what they were not looking for.

But they also found Josh Schulte's journals and now they were being read out in court. "I will bring down embassies and end occupations," Schulte had written. Why hadn't this made him like a Snowden or Daniel Hale, a principled whistleblower (at least to some) instead of a troll? Well, there was also the reference to fifty billion dollars, and about anger on telephone calls with his parents when his jail house essays like Malware of the Mind were mispublished on Facebook, followed by being apologetic.

Was it fair or seemly to use a person's diaries against them? They had gotten a warrant. In jail, unless you get a contraband cell phone, you can't speak without being recorded; Schulte couldn't take notes into a hidden virtual machine on a computer. So he kept handwritten journals and now here they were.

He'd written, "Give me a phone and a blog and I'll change the world." He hadn't. But had Collateral Murder, Manning magnum opus, stopped the war on Afghanistan? Or hadn't that some more than a decade later, a shameful pullout with translators rounded up and slaughtered, UN local staff left to die, Big Tony laughing all the way to Lisbon?

Court:

OK - US v. Schulte #Wikileaks trial Day 10, with MCC / contraband phone cooperator Carlos Betances still on direct; Inner City Press is covering the trial(s) and writing a book(let) about it

Assistant US Attorney: Mr. Betances, look at this message on the phone: "My case involves #Wikileaks and the #Vault7 disclosure." Did the defendant mention Wikileaks to you? Betances: I heard him talk about it once - Wikileaks. When I heard him talking, he stopped

AUSA: Did you hear him mention "Information War"? Betances: Yes. Informacion de guerra. Schulte: Objection. Judge Furman: Overruled. AUSA: Did you tell you about ProtonMail?

Betances: Yes, he said it was better, encrypted. AUSA: Was there a time they wanted to move the Samsung phone elsewhere in the jail? Betances: Yes. They were going to pay a guy called Flaco

$200 to take the phone to the library. AUSA: Did they tell you why? Schulte: Objection! Hearsay.

Judge Furman: How did you know? Betances: They told me. Judge Furman: Objection sustained. AUSA: Did you hear Mr. Schulte or Omar [Amanat] say why they wanted the phone there? Schulte: Objection! Judge Furman: Overruled. Betances: To send something out.

AUSA: The video you took of Mr. Schulte, what did you do with them? Betances: I told my lawyer about them then we met with the government. AUSA: When you met with the government, were you given any instructions about the cell phones? Betances: Not to do anything.

AUSA: Then what happened? Betances: They searched my cell. They found a cell phone and put me in the SHU [Special Housing Unit]

AUSA: Did inmates pass messages in the SHU? Schulte: Objection! Judge Furman: Overruled. Betances: By the ventilator. [Interpreted: A/C]

AUSA: What were you told? Schulte: Objection! Judge Furman: I want to hear it then I'll rule. Betances: They told me to stay silent and Josh and Omar would pay me $5000 for my silence.

Judge Furman: Objection overruled. AUSA: No further questions. Schulte: Good morning. Betances: Buenos dias. Schulte: You came from the Dominican Republic illegally, right? Betances: Yes. Schulte: Your grandmother paid for you to get in, right? Betances: Yes.

Schulte: At first you worked in a restaurant, right? Betances: Yes. Schulte: And that money wasn't enough for you, correct? Betances: Right. Schulte: You sold drugs to make more, right? Betances: Yes.

Schulte: You sold drugs in the Bronx with your brother in law? Betances: Yes. Schulte: You face live in prison if you don't cooperate, right? Betances: Yes, unless I get the [5k1] letter.

Schulte: You were deported and re-entered illegal with fake documents in Texas, right? Betances: Yes, correct. Schulte: What names did you use? Betances: Arturo Vasquez. Schulte: You didn't have permission to use his name, right? Betances: I had no permission.

Schulte: Your sentencing has been postponed, right? Betances: I don't think I was involved in that. Schulte: I withdraw the question. Your cooperation agreement on page 5 of 8 says the prosecutors will

forward your cooperation to immigration, right?
Betances: Yes.

Schulte: You hope to get an S visa to stay in the
country, right? Betances: Of course. And you have
asked me these type of questions twice now.
Schulte: Pleading guilty to having an illegal cell
phone was part of your cooperation deal, right?
Betances: Yes. Schulte: Your wife smuggled the
phone into the MCC, right?

Betances: Yes. Because the person who was
supposed to meet her outside wasn't there. Schulte:
You had your wife do something illegal for $500,
right? Betances: Yes. Chino deposited $100 in my
commissary.

Schulte: Let's talk about the phone you used in the
MCC. Betances: That WE used. Schulte: You
stored multiple phones for Omar because he let you
use them, right? Betances: Yes. And he promised to
pay me, but he never ever paid me.

Schulte: And I never paid you anything, right?
Betances: You did not. Schulte: In fact you knew I
had no money, right? Betances: There's no way to
know that.

Schulte: I move to enter this exhibit, to show that I did work for Omar [Amanat] and that the witness knows about it. AUSA: Objection. Hearsay.

Lengthy evidentiary fight ensues.

Schulte: You never saw drugs in the MCC? Betances: Usually I never saw them. Schulte: Did you witness Chino take drugs? Betances: No.

Schulte: No further questions. Judge Furman: Next witness.

Assistant US Attorney: The government calls [FBI] Special Agent Evan Schlessinger, was on counter-espionage squad.

Schlessinger: We searched Mr. Schulte's cell in the MCC in October 2018 with 50 agents.
Schlessinger: MCC detainee Carlos Betances told us Mr. Schulte had a phone. He showed us video of Schulte using the phone, and activity that occurred on the phone.

AUSA: GX 420 and 820-419. Have you seen these? Schlessinger: Yes. Photos provided by Carlos Betances

Schlessinger: It says, "My case involves #Wikileaks... CIA management had no idea what we did and could not possibly lead us." AUSA: Did you obtain additional search warrants to review Mr. Schulte's notebooks? Schlessinger: Yes. I recognize his handwriting

Schlessinger: Schulte wrote how they uploaded the wrong articles and his mother got upset and he spent the whole call apologizing. [His mother and father have been at the trial] Schlessinger: Schulte wrote, CIA not the only agency against Trump.

Schlessinger: Schulte wrote, if this is the way the USG [government] treats one of its own, imagine how they treat allies. I will close embassies and end occupations and jingoism.

Schlessinger: Schulte wrote, "Give me a phone and a blog and I will change the world."

AUSA: Back to GX 809, page 4. Can you read it? Schulte: I texted my dad from WhatsApp and Signal and finally got a response at one percent battery.

Schlessinger (continuing to read Schulte's notebook): Grow a pair and stand up to the bastards. Judge Furman: These are in evidence, jurors. It's up to you to decide what weight to give them. Schlessinger testifies that Omar Amanat was helping Schulte, to reach out.

Also, that they two wanted a single phone brought to the MCC library. Schlessinger (reading): China and Russia attacking US... Reality Winner... bartender for vendor...

FBI's Schlessinger testifies that Josh Schulte's Twitter account was "FreeJasonBourne."

[Just checked: Suspended]

FBI's Schlessinger (reading) "Jeremy Weber hacked the Atlassian and set up Josh Schulte. Schulte is the scapegoat because he reported infrastructure issues."

Cross examination. Schulte: You testified about Twitter, right? FBI's Schlessinger: Yes. Schulte: What there anything on that page? Schlessinger: Nothing but the photo. Schulte: Of Matt Damon? Schlessinger: Yes.

Schlessinger (reading) The Yahoo hacks were started as a result of this business dispute... And now, an American gulag. Schulte: Are you aware of this, written by Mr. Amanat? AUSA: Objection! Judge Furman: Sustained. Mr. Schulte, move on.

Schlessinger: We weren't particularly interested in these documents because they didn't seem to be about your case. Schulte: I am not part of Omar

Amanat's criminal case, right? Schlessinger: There is a forensic report. But no.

Schulte: Let me ask you about the government's WordPress exhibit. Judge Furman: Mr. Schulte, to finish with this witness I'll ask you not to use him to go over an exhibit that is in evidence. You'll have an opportunity to make those arguments to the jury.

Schulte: This document had nothing about Russia, right? FBI's Schlessinger: It did not. Schulte: It was about the criminal justice system, yes? Schlessinger: Parts of it were. Schulte: And the notebooks show a plan to re-write Malware of the Mind, right?

Judge Furman: We'll leave it there for the day. [Jury leaves]

Judge Furman: So let's talk about this proposed Defense Exhibit. It open for me, in Internet Explorer of all things. I didn't think Internet Explorer even existed any more. AUSA: We'll look into it.

Now AUSA says if Schulte tries to present into evidence his email to Federal Defenders, it will open up more waiver of privilege issues.

Schulte: It's that I sent it first to my lawyers, before sending it out more widely. Judge Furman: Doesn't make a difference.

Judge Furman: I'm expected a classified submission from the government. Adjourned.

XXI.

The scam of the United Nations, thought Kurt Wheelock long after he was banned, was that even those who should know better cited it when convenient. Kurt had been listening to Snowden's audio book - though he'd bragged that CIA complaints had made it number one now there was no competition in the NYPL, Kurt could renew it again and again, no other copies out - and winced not only at a pain in his stomach but one in his ears.

Snowden said the UN was for the right to online privacy and free thought. This while UNSG Antonio Guterres' chief censor Melissa Fleming took the Intercept's founders money to scrub the Internet of criticism of the UN, calling it disinformation, and refused to even answer Kurt's law firm pro bono letter seeking a dialogue for re-admission.

The UN was portrayed as the victim of spying while, as Kurt was finding, it collaborated and provided a platform for it, renting out its immunity in the same way as the UNOPS scam, the one before the current scam started by a retired UNCA Correspondent in her 5000 square foot inexplicable apartment. Wasn't that the size of UN Spokesman Stephane Dujarric's East 86th Street spread?

Kurt had stood underneath, live streaming then wondering if this was doxing, in the brave new world of Melissa Fleming. Her predecessor Alison Smale had false accused him of it, she like Fleming lived on taxpayer money on the Upper West Side high in the sky, call it public housing, like the mansion Guterres lived in on Sutton Place.

Kurt was hurt listening to the prosecution use Schulte's journals against him. Why had Schulte written these things down? But in prison he'd had nothing but time, even before the COVID lockdowns. And somehow it felt private, what you wrote in a diary, except perhaps from your significant other. Had Schulte ever had a significant other, other than the roommate he was awaiting prosecution for in Virginia? There were at least two books about Manning, and Snowden got paid to write (but not read) his own book. Nothing on Schulte. Nothing yet.

XXII.

They were sitting around in a hotel room: Ed Snowden, Glenn Greenwald, Laura Poitras and the guy were to to write out of the story, Ewen MacAskil. Ewen was asking Ed about his childhood. Rehearsed, Ed mentioned the coast guard down of Elizabeth City NC, then Fort Meade Maryland. Ewen took notes. Ed was a patriot, then.

Josh Schulte, no one interviewed. He sat alone in an apartment on 39th Street, just home from his soulless sell-out job at Bloomberg LP. He had a half dozen desktops and whirling servers, playing League of Legends and hiding photographs, they said, on his virtual machine. Then the FBI showed up. They too wanted to ask his childhood. But in a different way.

Where was Laura Poitras? Where was the Intercept and the fancy man from Hawai'i?

In the days they had in that Hong Kong hotel, Ed Snowden lying back on many-thread sheets spoke about his time in Hawai'i working under the mountain for Dell, then for Booz Allen, collecting documents, a glorified system administrator who talked about the fruit seller from Tunisia. He aimed to save the world from surveillance.

Schulte just wanted to get back at Amol, and Jeremy Webber, and maybe those a few steps higher. That was the line. And once they arrested him and had in, the second time, in the MCC jail, they sent in a jail house snitch offering cell phone access.

Carlos Betances gave Josh and Omar Amanat the cell phones, then filmed them using them. Soon 50 FBI agents descended on the MCC knowing just were to look and seizing Josh Schulte's notebook. They too were full of grand pronouncements, but not as palatable as Ed Snowden more scripted tome.

Ed said that democracy was key and TOR was the way to get it.

Josh said his bosses were incompetent and no one took his complaint seriously. They insisted on calling him Bald Asshole. He'd show them

Now jailed for years, trashed even by the one unauthorized profile. Not a hero but a troll.

Manning was already out of jail. The whistleblower circus had moved on. But here Josh was.

XXIII.

So who was a whistleblower,and who a mere leaker? Snowden self-servingly defined a leaker as a person of self-interest, as opposed to one intent on exposing government wrongdoing.

But Snowden also said he didn't self publish the document in order to not be seen as a crazy. Only a media institution, he said, could be objective. Really? Too much faith in institutions; the ultimate elitist, or ultimately an elitist. But who wasn't?

All of this bothered Kurt Wheelock. He'd been called a crazy at the UN; his most recent glimpse into the favoritism for the elite was that the New York Times' letters to unseal were docketed, once sent in by email and Fed Ex, while his were not, even a full week later.

He's figured out a way to file by ECF - but that required them to list you in advance as a filer on a case. He'd have to ask Michael Randall Long.

XIV.

What if Laura Poitras had pointed her camera on Josh Schulte, as she had on Snowden and the road to the Ecuador embassy? What would she have found? Instead, the video extant of Schulte was shot by the cooperator Carlos Betances, with a cell phone he (and the FBI?) had smuggled into the FBI. Schulte tries to keep it out of his re-trial, saying it's only purpose was to hammer home to the jurors that he was in jail. It was overruled. If Snowden was Citizen Four, Schulte would instead be known by his inmate number. For life, if the CIA had it's way.

The trial resumed after five days on July 6, with Schulte cross examining FBI Agent Schlessinger then calling three witnesses, starting with a former Federal Defenders paralegal he gave "Malware of the Mind" to for transmission to this FD lawyer(s). Judge Furman agreed to let it in, saying it was at least relevant to whether Schulte intended to release it to the public or to his lawyers.

Then Schulte called two CIA witnesses. Judge Furman said he would be sealing the courtroom, so Kurt Wheelock ran up and got in as the pool reporter. The first was "Cheng" - it is permissible, at least here, to say he was a young Asian man - and then Dave, an older white man who had testified at the first trial.

Schulte scored points with Dave, getting him to admit accessing Schulte's computer remotely, to having downloaded a version of Stash to a hard drive he store in his desk. Had he told the FBI about it this? No, it seemed.

Reasonable doubt, right? But when Kurt told another that Schulte scored points, the response was laughter. "Hey I root for defendants too sometimes," the person said. "But not Schulte. He's a scum bag."

Well. Kurt went on a pod- or vlog-cast, from the fire stairs and again asked, Why was Snowden a hero and Schulte just a troll? The vlogger mentioned the child porn. That, it seemed, had legs. More on Patreon here.

With the trial suddenly moving so fast, Kurt Wheelock wondered if he should speed up the projects he was working on. He had filed to unseal Schulte's civil case, but Judge Furman had not docketed much less ruled on that yet. Somewhere, out there, Michael Randall Long was digging. But would any of it be in time?

Kurt wondered how much to talk about the case, publicly. When he went on a vlog-cast from the fire stairs, the child porn charges were pointed out to him. Kurt shot back, But how do you know they are true? Maybe he'd gotten in too close.

Another case or precedent was raised to Kurt: that of Jeffrey Sterling, convicted on circumstantial evidence of leaking to James Risen. But as best Kurt would make out, he was released from prison in 2019. If convicted, how long would Schulte serve? Kurt found that Lev Parnas' co-defendant Igor Fruman, sentenced to a year and a day, got out in 50 days, a so called crisis furlough. Schulte wouldn't get that. But would he be found guilty? It might be decided by the end of the week, or the beginning of the next.

US v. Josh Schulte CIA #Wikileaks trial Day 11, FBI Agent Schlessinger being cross examined by Schulte.

Schulte: Good morning. Each of the notebooks you went through was 80-sheets, right? FBI Schlessinger: I think so. I don't recall.

Schulte: Let's pull up Exhibit 806. This is 160 total pages, right? Schlessinger: Yes.

Schulte: But the US choose only 2 pages, right? AUSA: Objection! Judge Furman: Sustained.

Schulte: And none of these pages were transmitted, right? Judge Furman: I think this has been asked and answered.

Schulte: You said my parents home wasn't raided, right? Schlessinger: Yes, I said that.

Schulte: But isn't it true that FBI agents visited my parents' home in Lubbock [Texas]? Schlessinger: It was not a raid. Schulte: But wasn't it unannounced?

FBI Agent Schlessinger: We were trying to get some classified info back, from your pro se application. [Note: Yesterday Inner City Press filed to unseal entirely withheld filings in Schulte's civil case - story later] Schulte: They confiscated computers, right?

 Schulte: Did you interview Michael? FBI Schlessinger: I was involved in one interview. Schulte: It says, CIA employee Michael was OK-ed for travel to Thailand. Did you ask for him to be placed on administrative leave? AUSA: Objection! Judge: Sustained.

Schulte: Michael was an employee of OSB at the CIA when I was, right? FBI Schlesinger: I believe so. Schulte: No further questions.

Judge: Re-direct? AUSA: Very briefly. Where there classification reviews of documents other than on WordPress? Schlessinger: Yes. AUSA: How about this email - was it classified? FBI Schlessinger: Yes. AUSA: Ms. Cooper, please go to [Exhibit] 801, page 3. Schulte: Objection. Beyond the scope and he has no personal knowledge. Judge: Overruled. Schlessinger: It was determined to be classified.

AUSA: No further questions. Judge Furman: Mr. Schulte? Schulte: Do you know if the notebooks found in my cell at MCC were ever shared with anyone? Schlessinger: No. Schulte: No further questions. Judge: The witness may step down.

AUSA: With two experts reports in, the government rests. Judge Furman: Jurors, Mr. Schulte bears no burden at all. I need to discuss legal issues, so I'll send you to the jury room. [Jury leaves] Schulte: I move to dismiss under Rule 29, especially on espionage

Judge Furman: Can you see more? Please distinguish between the Wikileaks counts and the MCC counts. Schulte: At the first trial I was specifically charged under the documents language... Now they have changed, to try to make it easier. Judge: It refers to... note

Judge Furman: So you're arguing that an electronic documents is not a document - and that an eBook [!] is not a book. I will reserved judgment but I am expressing my skepticism. Submit something, but your time is running short. Schulte: The statute is from 1945

Schulte: Look at the legislative history. Judge Furman: Any other issues under Rule 29, bracketing Count 9? Schulte: The Computer Fraud and Abuse Act, the US is alleging violations based on increasing unauthorized access. But I had a root server key.

AUSA: He received a memo. He no longer had authorization. Judge Furman: I agree. Rule 29 motion on that is denied. Now read my order about Count 9. Has stand-by counsel spoken to any potential witnesses? This would be the time.

Judge Furman: This would be the time to talk about the proposed testimony of Ms. Slotnik.

Schulte: It would show there was no intent to release without getting advice from counsel. And requesting advice does not waive privilege as to any advice given

Judge Furman: If it's labeled "attorney client privilege," I believe he can argue that he had no intent to release this information, under the attempt clause on Count 4. You can argue that he drafted tweets and set up a Twitter account so he had the intent.

Judge Furman: I think having Ms. Slotnik testify he drafted it for her is akin to marking it attorney client privilege. Am I missing something? AUSA: That he did something innocent with the document doesn't show what his other intent was. So it's not relevant

Schulte: It may not be determinative but it is relevant. The only thing about Malware in the notebook is about re-writing. For six months after I gave them to Ms. Slotnik there was not transmission.

Judge Furman: I deny the motion to preclude. Judge Furman: Remember, Mr. Schulte, you can not try to use the advice of counsel defense. [Note: "fancier" / at liberty defendant Trevor Milton of

Nikola is still mulling an advice of counsel defense for September trial Inner City Press will also cover]

Schulte: I will call witness(es) and rest today. Judge Furman: So you are not testifying yourself? Schulte: I am not.

[After a break in trial] Schulte: I'm going to call Ms. Slotnick, then CIA witnesses Chang and David. Judge Furman: Those last two are sealed witnesses under my order. [That Inner City Press opposed]

Now in semi-sealed courtroom as pool reporter under Order won, for CIA witnesses "Cheng" and "David."

Schulte: The defense calls Cheng. Where did you work from 2016 to 2018? Cheng: In CIA's CCI. As a contractor. Schulte: Did you work at the NSA during the Snowden leak? Cheng: Yes. Schulte: Were NSA policies stronger than DEVLAN? Cheng: Yes.

Cheng: I was surprised security on DEVLAN was not heightened. It was trust based. I heard, Wild Wild West Inner City Press @innercitypress · 1h Schulte: No further questions. AUSA: You used Atlassian, right? Cheng: Yes.

AUSA: But you don't know how much security was on Atlassian, do you? Cheng: I do not. Next witness: "Dave" Schulte: How did you describe DEVLAN? Dave: The Wild Wild West.

Schulte: Did you copy Stash into your home directory? Dave: Yes. Schulte: DId everyone have full_control? Dave: Yes. Schulte:

Did you copy Stash to an external hard drive that sat in your desk? Dave: Yes.

Schulte: Did FBI find the drive? Dave: I don't recall.

Schulte: Did you ever RDP, remote protocol, my computer? Dave: Yes. Schulte: No further questions.

Drum roll... Schulte: The defense rests.

Judge Furman: Summations tomorrow.

XV.

During the Josh Schulte charging conference, Judge Furman posed a hypothetical, one he said he had asked in a sealed conference. If a journalist in the courtroom for this trial heard Josh Schulte say something confidential, and the journalist knew that it was National Defense Information but thought it was in the public interest to publish it, would he or she be guilty under the Espionage Act?

In the sealed session, it seemed, the prosecutors had answered "Yes."

This made Kurt Wheelock stop and take notice. He had been in the position before, here in the SDNY. During the Larry Ray trial earlier in 2022, they had uploaded the list of Claudio Drury's prostitution clients. Kurt downloaded and put it on DocumentCloud, then tweeted the link.

The next day the US Attorney's Office asked him to take it down. First the DocumentCloud, then the tweet that still had its front page image. Ultimately Kurt published it in one of his booklets, like this one. But it wasn't National Defense Information.

So too with the name of Juror Number 4 in the Tim Shea / We Build the Wall trial. The name had been said and Kurt tweeted it. Later it was redacted in the transcript. But what was said was public. Wasn't it?

Apparently not in this CIA case, or any NSA case. How would it play out?

Kurt would publish, too fast to stop. But instead of faux politely asks, as in the Larry Ray trial, the prosecutors could finally just charge him. Get a grand jury to indict, then show up at his PACER terminal and handcuff. Send a message, so to speak.

Kurt would call Michael Randall Long, who would run over from his law office over the Ali Baba Fruit Market out on Worth Street. But because the Espionage Act was invoked, Kurt could essentially be disappeared. All the horror stories the leakers spoke about could come true. Kurt pinched himself to wake up. But it was still happening.

XVI.

The night before the Schulte closing arguments, Kurt Wheelock listened to more of Barton Gellman's Snowden book. He perked up when he heard an error (given his own penchant for typos). Gellman was recounting, perhaps to pad his book, a back and forth with Negroponte and McRaven at a conference in Aspen. Years later, Gellman says, he spoke with McRaven - and misidentifies who lost it in Aspen. Ah hah!

Kurt was at the UN when Negroponte represented the US there. A spook. The connections were growing, but the time was growing short.

* * *

It was the day for closing arguments, by the prosecutors then Josh Schulte, and Kurt Wheelock made it his business to get in earlier than usual. Assistant US Attorney Lockard laid into Schulte as a destructive nihilist, sneaking in to get the back up files and filing false complaints.

When Schulte's turn came he had a phrase, forensic artifacts, saying that the government's case lacked them. He asked, if he was really the leaker, why would he have complained so loudly? Wouldn't he have tried to fly before the radar?

The Google searches? They were part of his habits, as a computer geek. (The AUSA objected, and Judge Furman sustained). His apartment was raided, then his cell in the MCC. Sure some of the things in the notebooks were troubling. But, Schulte said, prison are bad places and he was losing it. Why not just charge him with contraband cell phone, and not espionage?

When Schulte finished, and the jury left, Judge Furman congratulated him and said depending on how things turn out, you might make a good criminal defense lawyer. Schulte laughed, and not hte forced ha-ha he deployed sometimes while cross examining. Judge Furman gave him a copy of the final jury charge, and said he'd see him the next morning at 9. So would Kurt Wheelock.

The closing arguments

OK- US v Josh Schulte CIA Wikileaks Vault7 closing arguments today (Day 12 of trial); yesterday it emerged DOJ thinks a journalist can be prosecuting for reporting what Schulte might say- Inner City Press is covering the case(s)

Judge Furman: Mr. Schulte, are you ready?

Schulte: I just need to be taken into the holding cell to change my shirt. Judge Furman: Fine. And please pull your mask up over your nose.

Jury entering! Judge Furman: Good morning, jurors. Yesterday's witness "Dave" is also "Dave C." And I have approved redactions to the transcript. Now, the closing arguments.

AUSA Lockard: On April 20, 2016, Joshua Schulte stole the CIA's cyber tools. He turned on the US.... Schulte had kept a secret cryptographic pass key and he tunneled through to that backup of all cyber tools. He stole them. And he transferred them to Wikileaks, knowing they would publish them. He bought computer equipment and did research.

AUSA: Schulte wiped his home computers and preserved only the data he wanted to keep. And on March 7, 2017, Wikileaks began releasing that data, as Vault 7 and Vault 8. It was devastating to the US. Overnight, cyber tools had to be shelves and re-written.

AUSA: This was all the work of Joshua Adam Schulte. You have seen devastating evidence uncovering the defendant's crimes. You've seen the computer equivalent of security camera footage. He deleted that video. When Wikileaks published, Schulte was IDed as suspect

AUSA: While at the CIA Schulte violated security protocols and filed false complaints. He left the CIA angry and disgruntled. So the FBI looked into him. During that March 15, 2017 interview, the defendant lied. He falsely denied leaking.

AUSA: Schulte was arrested and put into the MCC jail. He had phones smuggled in and set up social media accounts. He sent out sensitive information. He drafted a series of tweets with sensitive info and made arrangement to send out. But the phones were seized.

AUSA Michael Lockard: It was ego. And it was anger. Schulte would like to think of himself as a bad ass. But he was a nuclear bomb. He was called the Nuclear Option. He wanted revenge. He damaged the US' national security.

AUSA Lockard: DEVLAN was limited to 200 people in the CIA. As Anthony Leonis described, it contains the CIA's most sensitive cyber tools. It was closed and did not access the Internet. The information was "closely held" because of these protections.

AUSA: The "how" of what Schulte did can be complicated. There are reversions, deletions. But what he did is not complicated. The single purpose was to get access to the backup files and copy them. After April 16 [2016] he was not authorized to access the backups

AUSA: Schulte asked Leonis if he could keep his access. And he was told no. Politely, but no. Then Schulte changed his own project administrator status. OSB found out about this. Jeremy Weber raised the alarm: "We have a situation."

AUSA: It's like a bank manager finding that an employee was taking $20 bills from the cash drawer - and has a key to the vault. So they tried to take Schulte's keys away. Two IT guys came in and changed the passwords and SSH keys. Weber was there to test it.

AUSA: So as of April 18 Schulte knew he was not an administrator of any of the Atlassian products. He lied that his keys had been destroyed. And he Googled around about access to Confluence and Stash.

AUSA: If you'll permit me to paraphrase a little, Schulte was told, You are not in OSB anymore, keep your hands off OSB things. But he continued. He is, by analogy, figuring out where are the security cameras and how can I avoid them.

AUSA: I expect when Mr. Schulte speaks you'll hear --

Schulte: Objection - that's what rebuttal is for.

Judge Furman: Overruled. AUSA: He'll say there's no forensic evidence. But the files were copied and they were copied while Schulte had the ability to do it

AUSA Lockard: The fact there were is no footage inside the vault is not evidence that he did not go in there. Quite the opposite. He deleted the footage. He deleted log files on the OSB server with the RM Linux command.

AUSA: Schulte has suggested someone else was using his computer. But at the time of the transfer, he was in his work station sending chats and emails. Schulte was having trouble: his Brutal Kangaroo was failing, a tool was called Drifting Deadline

AUSA: As the complaints about Drifting Deadline mount, so do Schulte's problems with his co-worker Amol. He files a complaint and gets more isolated from his colleagues. He gets relocated. His frustrations are mounting. In April 2016 Schulte exploded.

AUSA: Once Wikileaks published Vault 7, our adversaries became very interested. It was devastating. Schulte was arrested and put in prison at the MCC. Don't consider that he was in prison, only what he did there. His journals says, I'll close embassies

AUSA: How would he close embassies and "end occupations"? His leverage is the classified information he has. He says he will set up a WordPress and stage his information war. Mr. Betances told you Schulte spoke about this information war, then stop.

AUSA: Schulte set up a Twitter account and wrote down the password. Then he started talking about Bartender. It was a cyber tool with a human who would get it on the target. Weber invited Schulte into it. In one draft, Schulte cites the vendor

AUSA: Let's talk about the grand jury subpoena Schulte got at Pershing Square. When he met the FBI they told him they were investigating the Vault 7 leak. He got a subpoena for his phone and testimony. So his false statements to the FBI were meant for the jury

AUSA: You'll be asked to find if this National Defense Information was "closely held." Schulte will say it was already public. Even if so, because he stole it and gave it to Wikileaks. It could still be closely held if US tried to protect it.

AUSA: I'm about to sit down. I'll ask you to do three things: pay attention, I think you have. Follow the judge's instructions on the law. And use your common sense. If you do, you'll find Schulte guilty of all charges. Thank you. [Schulte in 30. Watch this feed]

OK - break and strategizing over - Jury entering!

Judge Furman: Mr. Schulte, you may proceed.

Schulte: Mr. Lockard is very worried about the lack of evidence. There was no forensic artifact of a transmission to Wikileaks. No communications with Wikileaks

Schulte: They have investigated me for five years. And what? They cannot answer basic questions. They decided right away that it was me. On March 7, 2017 CIA documents showed up on Wikileaks. But the FBI said the theft was a full year earlier.

Schulte: They came to my apartment and seized even my Xbox. They found no government information. The spite motive is pure fantasy. I have devoted my whole life to service. I started as an intern at the NSA. I was an award winning developer.

Schulte: Frank Stedman called me "casually annoyed." Sean Roche called me calm. You saw four hour interviews of me - my demeanor was laid back. Play them again in deliberations. I may be litigious. I thought Ed Snowden was a traitor who should be executed.

Schulte: They told you I was nicknamed nuclear option. It had nothing to do with escalation. It is the opposite: the absence of emotion and speaking bluntly. I filed a complaint with security. Amol denied then admitted the allegations. An investigation kicked off.

Schulte: At that time, there were the Democratic Party emails, Guccifer 2.0, the Shadowbrokers... The diplomatic passport? I just forgot it, and so did they.

Schulte: I found I did not even have permission anymore to Brutal Kangaroo. I write to ten people. Leonis tells me I should have surmised he wanted me to pull out the sub component Shattered Assurance. It makes no sense. I got a letter of warning. I complain.

Schulte: I complain then find a job here in New York and move here. Why would have made myself a suspect, and painted a target on my back. It makes no sense. I engaged with EEO - a person who leaked in April 2016 would not do that.

Schulte: Mr. Leedom ignored all the weaknesses of DEVLAN. He's not an expert but an advocate.

There is testimony that the Alta Backups were not locked down. The potential suspect list is everyone who could sign in to DEVLAN, at least 200 people.

Schulte: Mr. Leedom says he had all my devices - but none of them were connected during the reversion period. Nothing. What am I copying the files to without a device connected to my computer? They do not have a theory.

Schulte: The government has no clue. That requires acquittal. The equivalent of 1000 hours of Netflix, in 75 minutes - is that possible? Leedom did not even have slide about it. This failure establishes reasonable doubt.

Schulte: According to the badge records, I tried to badge into the vault at 5:45 pm, from the bathroom. At 5:42 and 5:43 I'm in the bathroom. I wouldn't even be at my computer. I could not have copied the backup files.

Schulte: The government's own forensic experts have proven my innocence. The government cannot establish the steps necessary to commit this crime. I was in the bathroom during the access of the backups.

Schulte: How did I download from the bathroom? And how did I get it out? There are armed guards.

You have to badge in and badge out. They talk about Google searches. But I am a computer geek.

Judge Furman: This is not evidence.

Schulte: There is nothing unique about my activities. Mr. Berger is with the FBI. It's clear what team he is on. He zooms in and ignores the big picture. Look at my entire Amazon purchase history. Ask yourself, isn't their bias skewing their investigation?

Schulte: Mr. Berger tries to insinuate I must have visited the Wikileaks site because I downloaded TAILs. He tries to make much of a virtual machine. My purchases are consistent with my hobbies and habits.

Schulte: Brutal Kangaroo was a project I was working on at this time. There was nothing improper about having a folder named Brutal Kangaroo in my house. I was up late playing the League of Legends. I often stayed up late playing games. This is not uncommon.

Schulte: DEVLAN has no logs. Verizon gave them the logs of my home connection, and they gave them to me - and they established no connections to Wikileaks, much less the transfer of 200 gigabytes.

They did not even seek to introduce it. Reasonable doubt.

Schulte: Do you think the CIA tools I write leaves finger prints like this? If it did, I wouldn't have a job for long. Mr. Leedom admitted that malware can "time stump" files. I was an expert in Linux administration. I could have done it. But I didn't.

Schulte: Why would I leave a red flag like this? I wouldn't. When it suits them, they want you to believe I am an expert who can hide his tracks. Then they want you to believe I am a bungler. Which one is it? Because you can't be both.

Schulte: They have never proven this information went directly from the CIA to Wikileaks. And why would Wikileaks, a news organization, wait a full year? We'll have to wait and see what AUSA Denton says in rebuttal.

Schulte: You might ask, If it wasn't you, who was it? It is not my job to solve this crime. We are not the FBI. Look at the Wikileaks Task Force Report. They admit DEVLAN had no safeguards, that passwords were shared.

Schulte: The US cannot know who did it. They have not touched on foreign actors. It's like your home. If 100s of people have the key and your doors is open, anyone can come in. That's the CIA

Schulte: They focus on my writings, as if they could replace their need for proof. It's like a sacrifice bunt in baseball - they just try to move it forward. They try to dirty me up. I'm not accused just of phones in MCC - but of transmitting NDI.

 Schulte: Cell phones were everywhere at the MCC. But when I have one, they send 50 FBI agents. They are terrified - I have CIA and NSA information in my head. I could still do it. If I wanted to harm the US, I would do it. But in the videos of Betances, nothing

Schulte: What was I doing in the MCC? Drafting articles attacking the criminal justice system. I viewed it as an egregious violation, like all inmates do. I reached out. I wanted to prove my innocence. I was coming apart. Prison is not a nice place

Schulte: These prison writings were my hallucination. Look at the titles: Guilty Until Proven Wealthy. Does this sound like a battle plan? My plan was to prove I am innocent. Yes, I use a cell phone to try to get my story out to anyone who will listen.

Schulte: Did I use a cell phone? Yes. But that's not what I'm charged with. They charge NDI, to get you to believe I'm guilty of the Wikileaks conduct. Read it, Malware of the Mind - I'm talking about the justice system, how a non expert is so trusted.

Schulte: Look at my titles: tyranny - when I saw Information War - I write, I will open a WordPress account. My account is called Presumption of Innocence. You think anyone cares what I think about this? They don't. I am not declaring war on America

Schulte: Mr. Betances, like me, is in prison. Of course he tell prosecutors he heard me say Wikileaks and Russia. They want him to say that. He wants to get out to his family.

Schulte: You'll have a helpful chart to decide my fate. If you find they haven't proven an element, you move on. You can find me not-guilty quickly. Since I did not take the CIA backup, I could not possess them. You can easily move on.

Schulte: They are claiming I intended to leak NDI by writing in my notebooks, labeled "attorney client privilege." No one testified this was classified or NDI. What about the attempt? Hannah

Sotnik testified she gave it to my attorney. They focus only on page 84

Schulte: This is not National Defense Information -- Judge Furman: Ladies and gentlemen, it's my legal instructions which control. Go ahead. Schulte: This is a substitution that the judge approved for the transcript.

Schulte: The Bartender info was released on Wikileaks long before I wrote about it in my notebooks. I never even put the draft tweet in my Buffer account. They claim they swept in and stopped me from posting. But the US publicly disclosed it at trial

Schulte: If it was so confidential, why did they reveal it in this trial?

AUSA: Objection!

Judge Furman: Jurors, the government is not on trial here. Schulte: They did not call any classification expert. Judge Furman: Jurors, it's whether it was NDI at the time.

Schulte: I did not break in - I used my key. And reversion is like closing without savings. It is like an oil change. It is not theft. There was no damage to the Confluence VM.

Schulte: I'm going sit down now. My work is almost done. Your work is about to being. Ask yourself, do I trust these witnesses. If I were your relative or your friend, would this be enough evidence. It's not your job to fill their gaps. Schulte: This is my last chance to speak. You will have a chance to speak. All you have to say, What would Mr. Schulte say? You know all of it. My life is in your hands. I am convinced you will reach the verdict, I am innocent. Thank you.

Judge Furman: Ladies and gentlemen, we'll have another break before the rebuttal. All rise - jury exits. Judge Furman: Mr. Schulte, that was very impressively done. Depending on what happens here you may have a future as a defense lawyer. [Break of 30- story soon]

They're back - jury entering!

Judge Furman: Mr. Denton, you may proceed.

AUSA Denton: I get the last word. What Mr. Schulte said is similar to what he tried to get witnesses to say during the trial. But here is the chart of Mr. Leedom.

AUSA Denton: The reversion gave him back administrative access to the virtual machine. It's how he got to the Alta backups. Why was he deleting the log files? He was hiding what he did.

AUSA Denton: Mr. Schulte is trying to argue, I am too smart to have tried to steal it that way. It's obvious it was copied - it showed up on Wikileaks. Schulte says he couldn't have stolen before he was in the bathroom. But the door was steps away.

AUSA Denton: You know he stole it because he admits he did the reversion and what other reasons is there?

Schulte: Objection! Judge Furman: Overruled.

AUSA: Of the things he deleted, there are things we can't show. But his defense has been years in the making

AUSA: Schulte was ranting about Donald Trump and the FBI. He left up his Redress of Grievances. He can criticize the criminal justice system. But he talked about Bartender being in Wikileaks. That's not what matters - no one associated Bartender with that tool.

AUSA Denton: I am fond of John Adams' phrase, Facts are stubborn things. And they are stubborn here. Mr. Schulte took the back-up and sent it to Wikileaks. He is guilty. Thank you. Judge Furman:

We'll call it a day there and do the legal instructions tomorrow.

Judge Furman: Keep an open mind. Tomorrow after my instructions when you deliberate, there will be a lunch order form. Jury leaves. Judge Furman: I think we have all the exhibits except the WordPress returns and one of the notebooks

Judge Furman: Mr. Schulte, do you control your defense? Schulte: Yes. Can we get the final jury charge copy? Judge Furman: Yes. See you tomorrow.

* * *

During the break Schulte had stayed in the courtroom, practicing lines with "forensic artefact."

And when the came he deployed the phrase, and a clip from Mission Impossible with Tom Cruise. It was ironic, since the government had tried to charge him with pirating movies, too, after they searched his home computers. The child porn superseded that. If he were found guilty of espionage, would they even both with the child porn charges? And what would be the defense to that? Kurt Wheelock had proffered the one about a libertarian allowing people to upload anything to his server. Kurt had ideas how to proceed but not so much time, He got to work.

XVII.

With Friday morning being taken up with the legal instructions, a verdict seemed unlikely. But Kurt Wheelock rushed to the courthouse, by way of the UN where he filmed a stand-up with his phone, and proceeded to live tweet the jury charge, especially on what could constitute National Defense Information.

Could it already be public? Yes. To Kurt, this seemed like a problem. Should there be a privilege, then, for publishing anything said in open court, even if my mistake? Schulte had put in a letter, docketed late, asking sarcastically if a hot chocolate recipe could be NDI.

Finally the jury came out with a note, but it was only for a black magic marker. Then more substantive, they asked for the testimony of Patrick Leedom, formerly of MITRE, now of Microsoft. Why hadn't Shulte actually put on his expert as a witness?

Meanwhile during Friday's jury deliberations Judge Furman was still considering Kurt's application to unseal Schulte's civil case. One of those few following the trial asked Kurt, What civil trial? So by sealing, even that was hardly known. Kurt wondered, Would it get unsealed, or the request even docketed, in time?

Just before 5 o'clock on Friday, Judge Furman docketed and granted Kurt's Press application for unsealing in Schulte's civil case, except for one document still under review, Schulte's Habeus Corpus petition. Among the documents unsealed was Schulte hammering former Attorney General Jeff Sessions' October 26, 2018 memo to the MCC accusing Schulte of including classified information in a bail application. But where was Sessions' memo?

* * *

On what he knew could and probably would be the final weekend before the verdict, Kurt finished listening to Dark Mirror about Snowden. It was craven, he thought, despite or because of all the acknowledgements, including to the OSI, the Microsoft Foundation, and RCFP which time after time found reasons to not get involved in skirmishes for transparency, not only in crack conspiracy cases but also Honduras and Venezuela narcos getting tax payer funded lawyers, pedophiles and sex abuses withholding lists of clients and, of course, the UN.

Maybe Kurt was a bundle of resentments, like the subject here. Maybe that was the reason for the book, or books. The world overlapped but that didn't. Dark Mirror positively portrayed James Comey, speaking about national security at some Fordham Law School event. Kurt and Michael Randall Long, separately and/or together, had walked through that atrium, heading to and from The Bronx on the school's Ram Van, skipping the first part of exams to rant against banks and others from outside by Lincoln Center. The fancy backdrop of Manhattan, Robert Moses' handiwork.

Those screwed by cracked technology were so often from uptown. But they were invisible, in the whitewashed Dark Mirror. The fancy world stared at itself, self-congratulation at Turtle Bay. Then there were the outsiders, the misfits, the angry ranters. Ignored, misrepresented, aflame.

* * *

On the second day of jury deliberations in US v. Josh Schulte, literally nothing happened. In

Courtroom 15A hour after hour, there was nothing. Finally at 4:45 pm, there were the prosecutors, Schulte's two stand-by counsel, and in the gallery Schulte's mother. Judge Furman came out. He said "there has been radio silence."

The only request made was by Schulte, for time in the SCIF the following day, Day 3 of deliberations. Judge Furman said, Why not. The jurors came in. It didn't seem that they looked at Schulte. It seemed that his mother looked worried. Who wouldn't be?

In the docket of Schulte's civil case, mostly unsealed on July 8 after Inner City Press' request, entry number 2-1 still said "You do not have permission to view this document." Full circle.

XVIII.

It wasn't just that Snowden had been put on a pedestal while Schulte was jailed and forgotten, or reviled or mocked by most of those who remembered him. Even now, with Schulte being brought by Marshals to court each day and put in a suit to cross examine and now wait for his verdict, it was forgotten.

On July 12 Kurt came in to the courthouse early, for the second day of deliberations by the Schulte jury. But while Courtroom 15A stood silent and empty all day, upstairs Courtroom 23A caught fire.

It was that Jen Shah of Real Housewives of Salt Lake City, facing a trial on July 18 on telemarketing fraud charges, had decided to plead guilty. Outside, it was all documented by Bravo. But inside, even with the courtroom full, Kurt was the one to live-tweet it.

It was a routine proceeding, mostly - are you pleading guilty voluntarily, tell me in your own words clearly written out in advance by your lawyer why you believe you are guilty - but Kurt's tweets were pick up by People magazine, and the NY Post's Page Six, and Yahoo News which also did some national security reporting.

Surely Barton Gellman didn't know or care of Jen Shah. Probably not Snowden either - though Lindsay? Who knew. But neither did either of them even mention Schulte. The Brit Luke Harding referred once to a devastating leak of CIA cyber tools, before returning to the deeds of the GCHQ, logging the keystrokes of Turkiye's finance minister at a G20 meeting. Kurt had even checked out of the library in Chatham Square a graphic novel about Snowden. Would he have time to read it before the verdict?

* * *

On Day 3 of the Schulte jury deliberations, Kurt decided to head up to the courtroom around 10:30 am, skipping out on a no-live-question Federal Reserve session about the Community Reinvestment Act. On the 8th floor of the courthouse he saw the two prosecutors in the Schulte case as the elevator going up arrived. They declined to step in with him.

Up in the courtroom, Schulte's two in-person standby counsel were whispering to him. There had been a note, about what was a "substantial step." It was in the instruction about Schulte's alleged attempted transmission of National Defense Information from inside the MCC jail. Was drafting a tweet that was never sent a "substantial step"? Would putting it in a tweet-on-delay service change that?

Stand-by counsel put in a phone call to Ed Zas, still with the Federal Defenders, described on a guru. After a break, Schulte made some suggestions, and got a few in.

The jury entered, again not looking at Schulte. Judge Furman read the agreed answer to them. They would also get redacted copies of the Berger testimony. Were they close? Kurt was still looking into the Special Administrative Measures imposed by then-AG Jeff Sessions and, he was told, continued under Marrick Garland. Of chains and the SCIF.

Thread:

....Deliberations Day 3, there's been a jury question. Schulte, brought in by Marshals, is studying draft response. Stand-by counsel but not (yet?) his mother here Still waiting for arrival of Judge.

 AUSA asks Schulte and stand-by counsel, Are we all good on the Berger transcripts? So that's one of the questions.

All rise! Judge Furman: There's a question about my jury charge, what is a "substantial step."

AUSA: The jury's question is a bit inscrutable. Schulte asks for 5 minutes. Granted.

Schulte: Mixing substantial step with significant steps is confusing. AUSA: We like it.

Judge: I'm going to leave it as is. Schulte: Change "was" to "has already been" Judge: OK.

Jury entering! Judge Furman: You've asked about Jury Charge page 28, lines 18 to 22, about attempted transmission of NDI. As to a step, you may consider how many more remain [etc]

Judge Furman sends jury back to deliberate. Thread will continue.

Note: During the break about how to answer jury question about substantial step, Federal Defenders' Ed Zas, co-counsel & some say "guru" in Schulte's first trial, was consulted by phone. Now, what does a drafted but not sent tweet signify? A "substantial step"?

It's 4:45 pm and no verdict yet in US v Schulte - nothing from jury since question on "substantial step." Josh Schulte's mother is now here, but Schulte himself hasn't been brought back in yet.

Now cell block door opens. Schulte is brought in. He waves to his mother.

All rise! Judge Furman: No further notes, obviously. The week continues. Bring in the jurors (to discharge them).

Jurors enter. Judge Furman: Don't do any research. Adjourned...

* * *

As the jury deliberations on Josh Schulte's fate continued, for the second time, Kurt continued to stare at the memo Attorney General Jeff Session had sent to the MCC jail, that Schulte couldn't communicate with any media, in any way. How had that been legal? Who had even known about it? Where was RCFP, which represented Barton Gellman in his vanity FOIA lawsuit when he had funds and support from Columbia, the Century Fund, OSI and even Microsoft, been when the media was deprived in toto of a source accused of leaking information about CIA misdeeds and malware? Did the source's presumed motives really matter so much?

Now, during Schulte's time out in the light or at least the darknesses of Courtroom 15A, DOJ was acting more accommodating. Why of course they didn't oppose Schulte going again - one last time? - to the SCIF with his stand-by counsel. Schulte was allowed an extra minute to speak to his mother after the jury had been sent home for the day. Kurt paced in the back of the courtroom, wanting to observe and report everything but feeling like a voyeur.

It was suddenly too intimate, this largely forgotten trial. That day the Daily Beast wrote about a higher profile Manhattan short eyes, and noted that Inner City Press had been the only media to cover that trial too. But this was about the CIA, and surveillance, a topic the books about Snowden said had lit up Twitter and the Internet, and public squares all around the world. The video footage used was now reminiscent of the January 6 Capitol breach footage now provided by DOJ. Even the trial of the fraudulent lottery lawyer, moved from SDNY to EDNY, was getting more play.

Jeff Sessions and his black-out order lived on, as Merrick Garland's SAMs. On consent, as in the law they say. But if there were prisoner who couldn't speak, or sealed courtrooms where some exhibits could not be used, how could you know?

XIX.

On the 4th day of jury deliberations in US v. Schulte, the jury was clearly getting close. They sent a note about the grand jury subpoena that Schulte was charged with ignoring and obstructing. That was Count 9, of 9. So Kurt got ready.

It was past 3 pm, and Judge Furman was doing an unrelated sentencing in Courtroom 15A, when Kurt got a message that there was a verdict. But what was it? He headed back to Courtroom 15A. And, by thumbs, live tweeted:

US V SCHULTE COUNTS 1 TO 9 GUILTY ON ALL COUNTS

There are 2 extra US Marshals behind Schulte, for a total of four. Jury exiting

Judge Furman: No sentencing date, given the other charges pending. Status conference set for July 26 at 3 pm. Adjourned.

Could Schultz, having been found guilty, now speak about what he did and didn't do, and why? What of the Sessions (now Garland) Special Administrative Measures.

Beyond this booklet, Inner City Press will stay on the case(s) including those of Julian Assange, and Edward Snowden. Watch InnerCityPress.com